GNOMES IN THE GARDEN

GNOMES IN THE GARDEN

Celtic Faerie Teachings

DAVID AND CAROL SWING

AVALON GROVE PRESS
Weaverville, North Carolina

GNOMES IN THE GARDEN: Celtic Faerie Teachings

Avalon Grove Press
223 Dula Springs Road
Weaverville, NC 28787

www.avalongrove.com

Cover art by Kris Waldherr
Cover design by Bárbara Negrón

ISBN: 0-9742394-0-2 (previously ISBN 0-595-12623-5)

Library of Congress Control Number: 2003094792

Second Expanded Edition 2003
First Edition published by Writer's Showcase 2000

Printed in the United States of America

TABLE OF CONTENTS

Who's Who

- ✧ *Ban* — Soil Shaman; thick, white hair and beard and bright blue eyes
- ✧ *Elowee* — Teacher; Gwladys and Henry's daughter, dark hair and dark brown eyes
- ✧ *Nigel* — Ban and Elowee's son; young boy in Human years, dark hair and bright blue eyes

- ✧ *Willie* — Gatherer; winged, red hair and green eyes, blind but sees with spirit eyes
- ✧ *Goldie* — Gatherer; winged, blonde hair and golden brown eyes
- ✧ *Dawn* — Willie and Goldie's daughter; young girl in Human years, red-blonde hair and golden brown eyes

- ✧ *Thurisaz* — Warrior Priest; white hair and beard and dark brown eyes
- ✧ *Brighid* — Priestess; golden hair and brown eyes

- ✧ *Algiz* — Warrior, Commander of the Gnome Army; Thurisaz and Brighid's son, black hair and beard and brown eyes
- ✧ *Elfia* — Gnome Library Keeper; red hair and hazel eyes
- ✧ *Duncan* — Elfia and Algiz' son; young boy in Human years, red hair and green eyes

- ✧ *Henry* — Priest, Artist; salt and pepper hair and beard and brown eyes
- ✧ *Gwladys* — Priestess, Author; brilliant white hair and brown eyes

- ✧ *Esther* — Healer; Henry and Gwladys' daughter, red hair and green eyes
- ✧ *Jürgen* — Healer; blonde hair and closely-groomed, blonde chin beard

- ✧ *Angus* — Traveler; Gwladys' father, black hair, black beard and dark brown eyes
- ✧ *Kat* — Traveler; Gwladys' mother, brownish-blonde hair and hazel eyes

GREEN CAP GNOMES

- *Charlie* — Nature Nurturer, Elder; curly black hair and brown eyes
- *Renie* — Nature Nurturer, Elder; brown hair and brown eyes
- *Bonnie* — Renie and Charlie's daughter; very young child in Human years, golden blonde hair and hazel eyes

- *Rebecca* — Instrument Maker; silver hair and hazel eyes
- *Lorithoth* — Instrument Maker; gray hair and beard and hazel eyes

- *Zoeser* — Tunneler, Jewelry Maker; curly black hair and dark brown eyes
- *Telia* — Tunneler, Jewelry Maker; black hair and hazel eyes

ELVES & HUMANS

- *Manannán* — Celtic Sea God and former High King of the Elves, now a Traveler between realms; Ealilithea and Niamh's father; dark brown hair, short beard and dark brown eyes
- *Áine* — Celtic Goddess and former High Queen of the Elves, now a Traveler between realms; Ealilithea and Niamh's mother; dark red hair and green eyes

- *Arawn* — High King of the Elves; Merlin's brother; long, curly, black hair and dark brown eyes
- *Rhiannon* — High Queen of the Elves; reddish-blonde hair and blue eyes

- *Niamh* — Elven Lady of the Lake, Priestess, Advisor to Queen Rhiannon and King Arawn; Áine and Manannán's daughter and Ealilithea's sister; black hair and brown eyes
- *Yurigel* — Elven Lord of the Land, Warrior Commander, Priest, Advisor to Queen Rhiannon and King Arawn; dark red hair, closely-groomed dark red goatee and green eyes

- *Maurena* — Queen, Healer; red hair and green eyes
- *Nile* — King, Healer; dark brown hair, closely-trimmed dark brown goatee and brown eyes

- ✦ *Ealilithea/Nimuë/Carol* — Manannán and Áine's daughter and Niamh's sister; as an Elf, dark red hair and green eyes; as a Human today, blondish-brown hair and hazel eyes
- ✦ *Emrys/Merlin/David* — Arawn's brother; as an Elf, long, curly black hair, closely-trimmed black goatee and brown eyes; as a Human today, black hair and brown eyes

- ✦ *Arthur* — King of Britain in days long past; now returned as protector of the land and people of Appalachia both during and following the time of the changes
- ✦ *Gwenhwyfar* — Queen of Britain in days long past; now returned as protector of the land and people of Appalachia both during and following the time of the changes

OTHER FAIR FOLK

- ✦ *Brownies* — Greta Flowerfriend and Jack Surefoot
- ✦ *Centaurs* — Amera Trueheart and Lugh Strongarm
- ✦ *Sprites* — Mira Hummingbird and Gwionbach Dragonfly
- ✦ *Merfolk* — Demetra and Roth
- ✦ *Dragons* — Mons and Trill; Grandmother and Grandfather
- ✦ *Trolls* — Grief and Tears
- ✦ *Tree People* — True Tom

ANIMAL COMPANIONS

- ✦ *Polar Bear* — King of the Bears
- ✦ *Woodrow Woodchuck* — Professor
- ✦ *Benjamin Badger* — Physician
- ✦ *Wulf and the Council of Twelve* — Guides

Note: All Faerie eyes are attractively tilted upwards. Gnome ears grow into a point, but the top of the ear bends slightly away from the head. Elf ears also form a point, but lie close to the head.

Come away, O Human child!
To the waters and the wild
With a faery, hand in hand,
For the world's more full of weeping
than you can understand.

The Stolen Child, William Butler Yeats

INTRODUCTION

A group of the Celtic Faerie first introduced themselves to us in 1997. Though we did not realize it at the time, that meeting marked a major turning point in our lives. We did not understand why we had been chosen for such an unusual experience, and it took many months for us to become accustomed both to the reality of the existence of the Faerie and to their continued presence in our lives. As they shared more and more of their history, stories, and spiritual teachings with us, our view of the world changed so completely that we could no longer live safely within the bounds of traditional thinking. It was during this time that the Faerie first asked us to begin a book about their lives and teachings.

The pages that follow are filled almost entirely with the lives, adventures, and teachings of some of the numerous Fair Folk and spirit animals with whom we have become acquainted over the years. You will hear firsthand accounts of what life is like for those who dwell in the land of Tír na nÓg. You will also learn of the beliefs and sacred spiritual teachings of the Celtic Faerie, which bear witness to their great love for the Holy Mother and Father Creator and their son, Jesus. The adventures and life stories in this book are real, but you may also discover teachings layered within the stories, for that is the way of the Faerie.

The Fair Folk speak to us using the English language. They also often communicate telepathically with mental pictures to make certain concepts and events more clear. We have not attempted to incorporate their accents or colloquialisms from their own languages into the text, for to do so might have caused their teachings to become more difficult to understand.

Much of the information contained herein differs greatly from the traditional (and often unflattering) views held by Humans concerning the Celtic Faerie. We hope you will come away from this book with a new way of seeing, and that you will find within your heart a deeper sense of connection to the Great Mother Earth and all Creation.

Chapter I

The Elven Passage

Long ago, before recorded Human history, frequent battles erupted between the Tuatha Dé Danaan and the Human tribes, for the Humans sought to conquer and hold the Elven lands. These battles finally resulted in the migration of the Elves across the face of the Earth from east to west, as they sought safe havens where they could continue their way of life, free from the incursions of Humanity. All across the face of the European continent and, in fact, that of the world, you will find small Elven kingdoms scattered about like puddles of water left behind after a long and damaging storm. These puddles, or small kingdoms, were created as ripples in the fabric of Creation. Across the face of Mother Earth, these kingdoms could sometimes be found hidden far beneath an ancient mound; deep within a dark, primeval European forest; or high atop an area of mountainous terrain that, due to its inaccessibility, rarely felt the presence of Humanity.

Though some determined Fair Folk remained behind to preserve their relationship with their ancestral lands, many more were driven westward, ever westward, across the expanse of the European frontier. Finally, in a last futile attempt to hold their lands, they traveled across the ocean to Britain, the Isle of the Mighty; to Scotland and Wales; and to Ireland, the Holy Isle. These became the last strongholds of the Tuatha Dé Danaan before many were eventually driven into other dimensions further and further from the physical Mother Earth, to realms closer to the loving light of the Holy Parents.

It was also this last wave of Fair Folk who literally fled across the ocean to the isle of what is now called America in their desperate attempts to be free from Humanity. They found Humans there, as well, but these Humans had always lived in that land, and their hearts had not strayed far from the memory of the Holy Parents' love. Contacts were made with these first Humans, and with the native Faerie who had dwelt there since time immemorial, and the European Fair Folk found peace in that land for a time, at least until the invasion of the European Humans.

King Manannán, Queen Áine, and the Holy Grail

Arawn, High King of the Elves, begins the story of one of the battles between Humans and Elves.

"For most of our reign, there has been peace within our realm, for long ago we left the storms of battle behind—the battle between men and Elves. One of our last strongholds was the Isle of the Mighty, which you refer to today as Britain. While many of us who dwelt in Britain went into the mounds beneath the Earth, into the Great Mother's womb, some of us fled to Ireland, the Holy Isle. Even to this day, some of my people still dwell in these mounds in Ireland, on the Isle of the Mighty, and in northern Scotland.

"I and my beloved Queen Rhiannon were given the honor of escorting the Elven High King Manannán, his daughter, Princess Ealilithea, and the clans of his kingdom out of the physical realm of the Humans. King Manannán, upon the death of his wife, watched her spirit as she moved about the sacred mounds of Ireland. It was within these mounds that his kingdom lay hidden, and it was there that the Humans attacked us for the cauldron or Grail of plenty. They desired to possess the cauldron of immortality, the cauldron that would never boil a coward's meat. Were a soldier to be slain and placed within this cauldron, he would be born anew.

"The Humans forced their way into our land to seek this magical cauldron, but, after a bloody battle where many Elven and Human lives were lost, they came away only with a cooking pot with very few magical abilities. It would cook the food placed in it well, and, if it was used to boil medicines or herbs, their healing qualities would be slightly increased, but, overall and according to Elven standards, it was a very simple cooking pot and not very magical.

"The Grail of immortality they sought was not within our realm. Though it had passed into the physical realm, and we had seen it there ourselves, it had since moved into further realms where we had not yet gone. The Grail follows its own pathways and dwells where it wills. It is like the wind—no one knows where it comes from or where it goes. The Holy Grail could appear before your eyes one moment and be carried far away to distant realms the next."

Niamh, Elven Lady of the Lake in Tír na nÓg, continues the story. "My father and mother, with many of their court, were feasting deep within the forest groves. They were celebrating one of our sacred holy days, the Summer Solstice, and they felt magically protected. Humans often came to raid us in those days, for swords, pots, precious stones, and wives, but they had never before penetrated as far as my father's kingdom. In this last terrible raid, they came to my father and mother's kingdom in search of the legendary cauldron of plenty. These Humans had heard many tales of the cauldron from their tribal shamans, so they would send raiding parties time and time again in search of it. On this occasion, a cauldron containing food had been set up for the feast. With blood-curdling war cries, the Humans rode into the middle of that peaceful feast. Then, dismounting from their war chariots, they began to fight on foot, and a terrible and bloody battle began. Sadly, many of our people had come unarmed to the holiday feast for, in their prideful naiveté, they had not expected such an attack from the Humans so deep within their borders.

"My mother, Queen Áine, was spiritually powerful, but she encountered one of the Human warriors, who acted as a black magician shaman for his people. Even in the heat of that bloody battle, the Human magician was momentarily spellbound by my mother's beauty, but his greedy lust for power broke the spell my mother held over him. To gain his great prize, he killed my mother with dark magic. My father, King Manannán, in a fit of rage and grief, roared at the attacking Humans to take the worthless pot away, and he flung its boiling contents upon them. Overwhelmed with weeping, he gathered the still form of my mother into his arms. The marauding Humans had killed my beautiful and beloved mother over a simple cooking pot. As the cowards fled back to the safety of their realm, I do not doubt they gloated over their captured treasure. Being Elven-made, to them it surely appeared quite magically-empowered in their hall, and I am certain great and marvelous lies were told over this raid for that simple pot."

King Arawn continues, "It was a senseless loss, a tragic, wasteful death, and the King vowed to take vengeance on Humans. For three days, we grieved and sang mournful songs. No food or drink touched our lips, and the mound of our kingdom, ever bright, lay in gloomy darkness. On the eve of the third day of mourning, King Manannán, filled with wrath, was pacing about atop his royal mound. As he bitterly planned his attack upon the Humans to seek vengeance for the murder of his beloved mate, Queen Áine, he suddenly beheld her walking toward him. King Manannán was nearly overcome with disbelief and amazement, followed swiftly by profound joy.

He rushed forward to take his love into his arms, but she raised her hand in warning. She bade him halt and told him he could not embrace her now, for she was spirit, and, to be with her, he must travel with those of his kingdom farther and farther into the spirit realms, for only in those realms would he be able to rejoin her. The King, overjoyed at the promise of being reunited with his beloved queen, quite forgot his war of vengeance on the Humans and pursued his wife, ever before him but never near enough to touch and hold, deeper and farther into the spirit realms.

"Some of the Elven lords and ladies were determined not to leave their ancestral homes, so, with the King's permission, they remained behind to guard their realm, which lay close to, and in some areas overlapped, the Human realm. Others, including Rhiannon and I, followed King Manannán, traveling farther and farther into the spirit realms. During our travels, we were forced to fight many terrible and bloody battles with the Humans. More of our Elven soldiers volunteered to remain behind to guard our retreat from the barbaric Humans. After a period of seven and three days, we came upon a shining forest path. Though it was night in the realm where we dwelt, upon this path, dawn's sweet light glimmered through the tops of the trees and illuminated the fallen leaves about the tree trunks in gold. The light was so beautiful, and the birds sang ever so sweetly. The wind moved softly through the tree branches, and the leaves rustled with music. Then we heard Faerie voices singing, and we saw, with our own eyes, the Gnomes who had long since passed from the presence of our people and vanished into the mists of our own myths and legends.

"A group of Gnomes came forward to welcome us. We took them to be the elders, for the pure light of wisdom shining from their eyes nearly blinded us. Dressed in white and carrying their staffs, they asked us to follow them down their forest path of light. Proud King Manannán, being a man of cautious diplomacy, thought it best that at first we should camp on the forest pathway outside the realm of the Gnomes. He decided to send his advisors, nobles, and elders, including himself, to deal with the elders of the Gnomes. The King asked to meet with the Gnomes' king and queen, but the gentle Gnomes informed him they had not had a king or queen since leaving the Earthen realm, and that their realm was ruled by a counsel of elders.

"The Gnomes again beseeched the King and his company to follow them down the forest pathway. The King still hesitated, his reasons unknown even to himself, and he answered, 'I will not follow you down this forest pathway while I yet search for my wife, for I see her spirit always before me, like a deer who flees the hunter. I search not for her as a hunter who intends to do her harm, but as a loving husband who longs to embrace his lost love, for I have missed her sorely these past days. My heart is surely breaking, and I am near death from grief.'

"It was then that the King heard a voice calling to him. He looked down the forest pathway and saw his wife beckoning him. With a roar, he stood up and charged down the forest pathway, faster then a stag in full force, his heart bursting with joy. Close behind him ran their daughter, Ealilithea, nearly catching the wind by surprise in her great haste to embrace her mother. Weeping, the three held tightly to each other. Tears flowed down their cheeks, as they fell to their knees in disbelieving joy. For a time, we thought we saw a great cup standing in their place, and light like a waterfall poured into the cup and overflowed its sides. The water spread out and flowed to us and pooled about our feet. We felt strength fill our hearts and spirits and such love and compassion as were unknown to us before. With no thought of battle or war, our swords and shields resting useless in our hands, forgotten, we formed into companies and entered into the forest by the pathway of light.

"It was the Queen who led King Manannán, Princess Ealilithea, and us, as we followed behind, singing in an orderly company along the forest pathway. All about us ran Gnomes, singing, cheering, and playing their musical instruments. Winged Gnomes flew above our heads, cheering us on, and were joined by small, winged Sprites who flittered here and there about us, singing sweet songs into our ears, landing on our shoulders, brushing their small hands through our hair, and comforting us. Centaurs rode beside us, reaching out with their strong arms to support us. There were other beings of the Fair Folk there with us, a great company who traveled down the forest pathway. Daylight filled that realm, and all darkness was brushed away from our eyes.

"It was then we were led into a great, great grove of trees. There, in a large circular clearing, stood a stone pillar, and upon this pillar rested what we had come to know as the Holy Grail. Upon entering the Gnome realm, we had observed that the cauldron had taken on a different shape. Instead of the large cauldron we had known in the past, it appeared now as a drinking cup. It was still the same Grail we had known for thousands of years, the cauldron that had originated before our memories in myths and to the present day; yet it had somehow changed shape and become a cup, and we did not understand exactly what it signified. We had some sense of understanding, for, again, we did see the cup form with King Manannán, Queen Áine, and their daughter, Ealilithea, and we saw how the blessings of the Holy Parents flowed into it. We understood that this was the shape the cauldron, now the cup, was to take. It was the transformation of spirit, a new understanding, and though we did not comprehend what the cup signified, we had the hope that in the future the Holy Parents would share this mystery with us.

"It was nearly five hundred years before Christ's birth when the guardianship of the Grail passed from the Gnomes to the Elves. Except for a brief period when it dwelt within the Human realm, King Manannán, his Queen, and our people were the guardians of the Grail Cup for almost one thousand years. King Manannán would lead companies of warriors back into realms closer to Earth in an attempt to defeat the armies who strove to purge the very memory of the Holy Mother Creator and the Great Mother Earth from the minds of her children and from all Creation. We went to fight battles against the encroaching Humans to protect what we had, but we also fought to protect other Humans who were not cut from the same material as the barbarian Humans who held no light within.

"Our hearts were different then; before, we had waged war on Humans to exterminate them and drive them out. To be honest, we had not seen all Humans as our enemies. There were gentle Humans who seemed more Elven than Human, and it was for their sake we could justify our wars with others of their kind. This time, however, when we returned from the realm where we now dwelt, led by King Manannán, our hearts were different. No longer did we see most Humans as enemies. We understood they were misled, confused, and lost; that they had forgotten the Holy Mother Creator and were driving her presence out of their lives. They called always upon the male gods of war, seeing them and claiming them to be the Holy Father. It was these Human warrior tribes we fought against, in an attempt to free Mother Earth from their domination and to free the peaceful, gentle Humans who were trampled and crushed by the waves of marauding hordes from these tribes.

"Battle after battle we engaged in with the Humans, returning safely to our realm at night. Many lives were lost on both sides, and, though our people had long known what it meant to be immortal, many of our immortal lives were cut short with the thrust of the Human spear or the cut of the Human sword and ax. During one of these battles, King Manannán was grievously wounded. He lay near to death, his immortal spirit pouring from his body as his blood soaked the Great Mother Earth. Though a Human hand had driven the spear point deep into the King's groin, the spear the Human used was a gift provided by the Evil One. It was the same spear used to pierce the side of Christ as he hung upon the cross."

Rhiannon, High Queen of the Elves and Arawn's sacred mate, continues here. "As the King lay on the battlefield slowly dying, his beloved companion, Queen Áine, appeared with their two-month old daughter, Niamh, in her arms and their other daughter, Ealilithea, beside her. She grieved to see the pain and suffering of her husband and instructed his general and his company to place the King on a bier and bring him back into our realm, for only there would he be able to survive such a great wound. My beloved husband, Arawn, led the King's troops as they fought their way back to the realm of light, protecting King Manannán, as he lay helpless on his hastily erected bier. We had hoped our mighty King could be healed in the Gnomes' realm of light, and it is true the Gnomes possess magical healing powers that allowed King Manannán to live. Sadly, however, even the Gnome doctors could not heal him entirely, and he spent many years lying in bed, unable to move and suffering.

"For many centuries, the grievously wounded King ruled his kingdom the best he could with the help of his Queen. He strove mightily with all his heart to provide sound judgment and to be a fit ruler for his people. Sadly, some days the King could do little more than sit up in bed, but on better days, he was able to leave his bed to be carried about on his wooden throne from place to place, as he tried to take part in the lives of his people, both the nobles and those who worked the land. He wanted desperately to be there to talk to them and meet all their needs, no matter how great or how small, to hear their voices and their concerns and care for them, though he himself was the one who needed the most care. He watched his youngest daughter, Niamh, grow older and become a young woman, trained by her mother and then by her sister in the arts of a priestess. He watched both his daughters grow into beautiful young women and felt pride at their achievements and their grace and beauty. The High Queen and King chose to pass over the day-to-day tasks of running the realm to my husband, King Arawn, and myself. As time went on, we assumed more and more of their responsibilities, and, eventually, we were named their successors.

"During one of the Gatherings of the Grove, we prayed to the Holy Mother and Father and their son (who, by that time, we had come to know as Jesus), asking what could be done to ease King Manannán's pain and suffering. We were reminded that he was the guardian of the Grail and the protector of the realms, and the only way to release him from his suffering was for the Grail Cup to pass into the Human realm and for a worthy Human to become its guardian. The Grail Cup used by Jesus during the Last Supper is the same cup that caught a few drops of his blood as he hung upon the cross. It was brought to the shores of the Isle of the Mighty for a brief time after Christ's death by Joseph of Arimathea, but, after Joseph's death and with the onslaught of the Romans, the cup withdrew back into the spirit world, where King Manannán had become its protector. Now the cup was to pass from his responsibility and move once more back into the physical realm. Once the cup had returned, a Human, a simple Human who would be considered a fool, would learn the secrets of the Grail and become the Grail's new protector. Then and only then would King Manannán be released from his suffering.

"Ealilithea, King Manannán's eldest daughter, had become wedded to one of Arawn's brothers, an Elven prince named Emrys. For some time, Emrys had been fascinated by the Human world. He spent much time watching Humans, and he had found a number of friends among them. Ealilithea, on the other hand, had suffered a very disagreeable experience some centuries before when she had agreed to be born as a Human in an attempt to help ensure the survival of Christianity.

"She was born into a family of Roman merchants as a male named Lucian at a time when Christians were much persecuted. Lucian, ignoring the disapproval of his family, embraced the Christian faith, a decision that could easily bring death at that time in history. He married soon after and began to raise a family. Lucian's wife became a friend to a woman named Helena. Through that friendship, Lucian also came to know Helena, and he spoke to her of the mission of Christ. Not too long thereafter, Lucian became one of the many Christians persecuted under the reign of Emperor Diocletian, and he, his wife, and their two children were torn apart by lions in the Coliseum arena in Rome. Their friend, Helena, became a much-valued advisor to her son, Constantine, the Great. During Emperor Constantine's rule, Christianity became recognized as one of the official religions of the Roman world, thus freeing its followers from persecution.

"Ealilithea retained quite a vivid memory of her life and painful death in Rome, and she was not so keen on returning to the Human realm; still, she did not wish to watch her father continue to suffer. Thus it was that Eali-lithea and Emrys volunteered to enter the Human realm together to prepare a court that would not only release King Manannán from suffering, but would help secure the memory of the Holy Mother and the Great Mother in the minds and memories of male-kind. They went to prepare a place where Humans would no longer be capable of cruel injustice, but might learn instead to hear the Holy Mother and the Mother Earth's cry of compassion, and remember and honor them, as they remembered and honored the Holy Father and the son."

King Arawn concludes, "Through the guidance and blessing of the Holy Parents and Jesus and Mary, Emrys and Ealilithea were born as Humans and had the rare privilege and good fortune to become members of King Arthur's court."

Lost in the Sea of Humanity

Carol takes up the story here. "Emrys, the first to be born, was given the name Merlin, while Ealilithea followed some thirty years later as Nimuë, the youngest of King Arthur's three half-sisters. The legends of King Arthur's court have been told and retold by many talented writers, but they have not been recounted with complete accuracy. The Fair Folk themselves watched many of the actual events unfold, and their recollections often differ from the legends. We hope, in the future, to write of the Arthurian days as witnessed through Faerie eyes.

"When Emrys and Ealilithea passed on from their Human lives as Merlin and Nimuë, they returned to Tír na nÓg with the uncomfortable knowledge that their mission had not been a great success. It was decided some years later, during a Gathering of the Grove, that Lili and Merlin (as they were often referred to now by the Fair Folk) would return to the physical Earth once more. The Fair Folk hoped they might find a way to help Humans remember the long ago days when all those who dwelt on Earth lived together in peace and spoke but one language, the language of all Creation. They thought perhaps if Humans were to remember those days, they would once again learn to speak with the Holy Parents, Christ, and Mary and, in so doing, would begin to seek ways to bring healing to the Great Mother Earth. They feared that if Humanity did not change, the Holy Parents would act forcefully to prevent Humanity from completely annihilating all life upon the Earth.

"When Merlin and Lili again returned to the physical Earth, they became lost in the sea of Humanity, no longer remembering their original identities. They were reborn many times as many different personalities, swimming forward and backward in the sea of time. Sometimes they would remember bits and pieces of their past lives and find themselves drawn to the ancient nature teachings or toward Christ and Mary. Because of these leanings, they often became priests, priestesses, wise women, nuns, or monks, but they usually found it difficult to follow traditional church doctrine. The result was often torture and a painful death at the hands of those who did not care for their non-traditional beliefs or teachings. When they died, they would pass on to an area of heaven that reflected their beliefs during the lifetime they had just completed. Soon, however, they would begin to wander about in search of new adventures, until, with the aid of spirit guides, they would eventually choose another life and return to Earth once more. Merlin and Lili continued to be reborn as Humans over and over again for more than one thousand years."

Gwladys, a beautiful Gnome elder and priestess, tells of their present lives. "When Merlin was born into his current Human life, he had forgotten his Fair Folk heritage. The dear faces of his Elven and Gnome families no longer filled his memories, nor did his thoughts ever turn to the bright and sunny land of Tír na nÓg.

"Merlin was born to a single mother. Emotionally a child herself, she would travel from place to place with her small son, seeking a mate to be her lover and to take responsibility for the child. After several attempts and failed relationships, she appeared early one morning upon the doorstep of the parents of her last lover, who had unthinkingly divulged to her the address of his parents' home. The desperate young woman knocked on the door of these bewildered, kind-hearted people and pleaded with them to give both her and her child shelter, at least for a short time, while she attempted to find work. For several weeks, this young woman and her son dwelt with these kind-hearted Samaritans. Passing more and more of the responsibility for the care of her child to her female hostess, the young mother finally took her leave and fled to parts unknown. The couple raised this abandoned child for fourteen years and accepted him as their own son.

"Though the child we refer to as Merlin, known to this couple as David, was aware that he was born to other parents, he gave little thought to them in his young life. All would have been well, and he would have flourished under the benevolent love of his foster mother and the stern guidance of his foster father, but the circumstances of his past life would not make allowance for this, for, in being the Merlin, his spirit held a special and unique light. This light captured the attention of wandering spirits, who flocked to him like moths to a source of light. The young child, not understanding what was required of him by the disembodied spirits, was terrorized by the faces of these frightening specters in the darkness of the night. After a time, the house he lived in became quite haunted by spirits who had come to visit and then decided to stay to torment this small boy.

"His foster parents did not completely comprehend what was happening, but, in their own way, they felt these presences, and this created a sense of unease within the household. His foster father wanted no part of the business, and a gulf appeared between him and David, which widened eventually to a nearly impassable chasm. His loving, foster mother, a precious gift from the Holy Family and a confidante of the Holy Mother herself, began to obtain books on the occult and to look into matters of the supernatural. Though she strove mightily, she still could not understand what was happening. As the hauntings upon David increased both by day and by night, the visits became more terrible, and the emotions of the sensitive, young boy began to fragment. His foster parents did not understand and believed his behavior to be merely the emotional state of a young boy and not a condition caused by the unseen presences in his life.

"The young Merlin, or David, if you will, spent much time in the hills behind his home, for, when he was outside, he took comfort from the sun's warmth and light. Neither did he fear the soft, comforting light of the full moon in the night sky, for it was out in the elements of nature where he gained strength to carry through with his difficult, young life. Though he sensed our presence with him then, he could not quite see us, for he had shut his spiritual eyes in an effort not to see the frightful visages of his unwanted, ghostly visitors. At times, when he was alone in the hills, he would smell a sweet perfume or feel gentle fingers caress his hair or his face and hear quiet, whispered words of love and reassurance from us. He did not know where these comforts came from, but they would fill his heart with great joy, and, in those moments, he would run, striving mightily to outpace the wind and make that joy last forever. There were nights when, in the wee hours of the morning, unable to tolerate his unwanted phantom guests, he would slip outside and venture into his beloved hills to look up at the twinkling stars high in the heavens or to gaze fully into the face of Mother Moon. There, also, we would come to him, whispering words of assurance and trying to calm his trembling, lend him strength, and teach him to open himself up to the love of the Holy Family, so he could triumph over the unfortunate snare placed there by the Evil One in which this young boy now found himself entrapped.

"To add to his torment, it was at the peak of these dreadful hauntings that Merlin was visited by an evil spirit who took the form of a fair-faced, dark-haired young woman. During these dreadful visits, we would try very hard to shield him from her evil; yet how could this young boy comprehend the seductive wiles of this ancient, malevolent spirit? At night, as he tried to sleep, horrible battles would rage about him as we fought against her and her minions. Dreadful scenes of carnage would fill his dreams, of long ago battles from his own past lives, from the lives of those frustrated spirits who surrounded him, or from our own battles against his evil seducer.

"During the last of these battles, in the early morning, just after the sun had risen and the first rays of sunlight had filtered through the half-buried window of his basement bedroom, in the room next to him, this evil spirit, enraged by the presence of his Faerie family, expressed her fury. Her long, terrifying, banshee wails caused David's heart to beat so rapidly in his chest that he feared it would explode. At that moment of great danger, we appeared before him again, and he saw us for the first time in this lifetime. We frantically warned him to flee upstairs to safety, for this terrible spirit, in her extreme wrath, was about to cause him great, bodily harm. We, in our efforts to protect him, literally pulled him from his bed to the floor and dragged him up the steep, narrow steps to the rooms above. Frightened and bewildered, he begged us to leave him alone, for he did not see us as much different from the enemy or his ghostly visitors of the night. At that moment, he shut more firmly his spiritual eye against us and all things of the spiritual realm. Though he never lost his interest in things of the super-natural, he did manage, in some way, to block the unwanted visits of his phantom guests.

"When David turned fourteen years of age, his foster parents determined they would officially adopt him. The law required that David's natural parents be notified before the adoption could be completed. Upon learning of his son's whereabouts, his natural father determined to reclaim his son and teach him the ways of salvation as practiced by his deeply fundamental Baptist church. Removed abruptly from his boyhood home in Wyoming, David was transplanted to the western part of the United States, where he spent the next three years with his newly-met father, stepmother, and four younger siblings—two brothers and two sisters. True to his promise, his father made certain David was thoroughly indoctrinated into the ways of the church. Ironically, this new religious training placed a rigid block between him and the ways of Spirit. In response, he finally cut himself off totally from the Holy Parents and lost all contact with the things of Spirit and even with the secrets of his own heart. For several painful, spiritually-deadened years, David struggled to survive in this harsh environment, until finally he once again came across his lost love, his soul mate of long ago, Ealilithea, who, in this life, was known by the name of Carol."

Carol continues here, "I was raised in a small town in northeastern Pennsylvania. I first learned about reincarnation at the age of twelve from a book written by Ruth Montgomery. From that moment on, I had no doubt reincarnation was a fact, and I longed to learn of my own past lives. I was brought up in the Moravian faith, but the minister was unable to teach me about reincarnation, for it is not contained within the standard Moravian religious doctrine.

"Small town living did not provide what I wanted from life, so, shortly after graduating from high school at age seventeen, I left home to move to Atlantic City, New Jersey. I arrived there just in time to experience the introduction of casino gambling to that formerly peaceful seaside town. Though casinos were rather exciting, they could not compete with New York, my dream city, so, after two years in Atlantic City, I left for New York City, where I lived happily in Manhattan for several years.

"Though I loved the excitement of New York, I began to feel a certain spiritual emptiness, so I made an appointment to visit a psychic, hoping she could help me determine my next step in life. She told me details from some of my past lives and mentioned a spiritual teaching that spoke openly of reincarnation and spirit travel. Hoping this would help me in my spiritual quest, I soon located a book written by the teaching's founder, an American who claimed to be a spiritual master. I was excited by the promise of spiritual enlightenment, for, in those days, the new age movement was still in its infancy, and the options available for a spiritual seeker were much more limited than today. I was reasonably content for many years with this organization's intimation that higher initiations would one day provide me with the enlightenment I still lacked. After a time, however, my nightly dreams made it clear to me that I was looking for enlightenment in the wrong place, and so I took up my spiritual quest once more.

"After seven years in New York, I felt an undeniable urge to move to the western United States. A female friend had recently relocated to Phoenix,

Arizona, so I packed up my belongings and moved to the desert. Since I had acquired a number of years of experience as a legal secretary in New York, I soon found employment at a large law firm, one that occupied several floors of a skyscraper in downtown Phoenix. In the elevator one day, my eyes met David's. Though we had never met before, he seemed familiar to me. A friend at work knew David and told me he worked on another floor of our law firm. She asked him to attend a movie with the two of us, but she purposely backed out at the last moment, leaving the two of us alone for our first date.

"The night we met, David had a dream. He saw a woman with long, red hair cascading down her back, mounted upon a large, black horse. She was a priestess, and she caused a sense of unease in those around her. He was dressed as a warrior, and she was bidding him farewell as he left for a battle. Some years later, I dreamt that I reached inside a closet beneath a stairwell, drew out a box, and opened it. Within the box, I discovered the head of a warrior in a warrior's helm. Directly behind me, I heard a deep, powerful voice, which, in the dream, I recognized as the voice of Merlin. His words echoed in the silence, 'It is almost time for Arthur to awake.' Without turning around, I carefully put the cover back over the head in the box and replaced it under the stairwell, but closer to the front than it had been before.

"David and I were married six months after we met, although I knew he was the one for me much sooner than that. A few months after our marriage, we left the desert behind and moved to North Carolina."

CHAPTER II

Meeting the Gnomes

Gwladys takes up the story again, "For the first years of the couple's marriage, their lives dealt more with struggling to survive in the physical world than with spiritual matters. Shortly after their tenth anniversary, however, when David was nearing the age of forty, their life together took an unusual turn.

"For many years, Merlin had shut tight the doors of his heart against the voices of the loving Mother and Father Creator. He no longer traveled to his heart well to sip from the living waters placed there by the Holy Parents to renew and refresh his spirit. So frightened had he become of anything spiritual that he avoided any form of prayer, meditation, contemplation, or any spiritual tool that might have brought him in contact with his heart as a source of spiritual renewal. Therefore, since he would not listen to the voices of the Holy Parents, Christ, or Mary, we had little hope he would listen to our voices either. We had, upon many occasions, observed him watching what modern Humans term 'television' or what we refer to as the 'evil eye.' We noticed that, during the times he watched the evil eye, his conscious mind was distracted by the television, while his spiritual self was possibly open to our approach. It was after many Gatherings of the Grove, much discussion, and many prayers that we decided the best time to try to reach him was, ironically, during the moments when the Evil One held him most firmly in his hypnotic spell—while he was watching his beloved television."

When not otherwise noted, David is the narrator in the following chapters.

One night, as I sat slumped on the couch watching television, out of the corner of my eye, I detected a movement. I assumed it was my wife, on her way to complain about my choice of shows and urge me to turn off the television. I became rather annoyed and determined to watch the show to the very end. I noticed another movement, and, suddenly, a little man strolled into my line of sight and planted himself squarely in front of the television set. Startled, I took my eyes from the screen and looked directly at him.

I saw a small man who stood slightly over waist-high. His ears came to a point and curved downwards at the tip, and he wore a bright red, conical-shaped cap. From beneath the cap, thick tufts of white hair escaped to merge into his long, white beard, which ended in a curled point at his waist. The white hair of his untamed, bushy eyebrows could not conceal the look of kindness in his clear, blue eyes, and, within his great wilderness of white beard, a large-toothed smile could be seen. He was attired in an old-fashioned, bright blue breech coat with large gold buttons running down its front. Over this, he wore a wide belt with fine scrollwork etching, and I barely glimpsed a flash of yellow shirt peeking out from beneath his long, white beard. As I glanced downward, I saw he wore gray breeches with red pinstripes and long yellow hose, ending in a pair of bright green shoes that curled up at the toes.

The short gentleman removed his red cap and, making a curious little bow, said, "Hello, lad. Please let me introduce myself. My name is Ban."

I glimpsed movement again to my left, and into my line of sight stepped a young woman a little shorter than Ban. I noticed first her sparkling, brown eyes and the compassionate, loving look in them, and I was taken aback by her breathtakingly beautiful smile. The modest blush in her cheeks offset her smooth, creamy complexion. Her long black hair was parted in the center, braided in back, and held by a hair clip in the shape of a gold leaf, which encircled a large white pearl. Her gold bodice was laced closed by golden cords, and a stitched pattern of six Celtic knots, with three knots on each side, descended down its front. Her long dress was royal blue in color with wide gold trim on the sleeves and a narrow gold border on its hem. Her feet were covered by matching gold slippers, and on her head perched a red cap with a complex design embroidered in gold.

"This is my wife, Elowee," Ban proudly declared, and Elowee curtsied gracefully.

I decided I had drifted off into a dream, so I replied, "That's very nice," and I turned back to the flickering images on the television screen.

They were rather amused by this, and Ban told me, "We will see more of each other very soon." Then he bowed, Elowee curtsied sweetly, and they walked out of my line of sight. I returned to watching the show.

The next morning, as I staggered toward my truck to drive to work, my eyes barely open, I saw them in the front yard. They greeted me again and wished me a blessed day. When I returned home from work, they met me in the front yard again. I began to realize they were not just a dream. Their voices, the way they looked, their facial expressions—everything told me they were quite real. I did not want to accept it, but they greeted me every day of the week as I left for work and again when I returned home. They greeted me when I walked the dog or when I sat on the back porch. It was from this simple beginning that our relationship grew. Over time, I began to trust them and finally came to believe they really cared for me. They told me they loved me and considered me their son, for they said they had adopted me at a time in the very distant past. I later learned there are also Gnome children, and that Ban and Elowee have a son named Nigel. Nigel has the black hair of his mother and the bright, blue eyes of his father, and he refers to me as his big brother.

Ban, Elowee, and Nigel

Ban is a farmer and one of the Gnomes in charge of ensuring that his village's vegetable garden is growing properly. I coined the term "soil shaman," and he agreed that, in our language, it is a relatively close translation. Ban speaks here of how he spends his days.

"I am a simple farmer, given the blessed task of helping to provide food for our small village. The ways of a farmer in our realm are much different from those of a farmer in the Human world. We have an intimate relationship with our Mother Earth, as strong a bond as that which exists between a mother and her children. Like good children who wish to please their Mother, we draw close to her that we may hear her words, feel her breath upon our face, and listen to her counsel, that she may guide us as we go about our planting. We agree with the Human phrase, 'Cleanliness is next to Godliness,' and yet, when it comes to farming, no Gnome will shy away from the chance to have the Mother Earth's soil upon his or her clothing when planting seeds for future crops.

"To be a proper farmer, you must use all your senses. Drawing close to the soil of the Mother by getting down on your hands and knees, with

reverence, you send the energy of your fingertips like plant roots, deep
within her rich earth, to search out the nutrients and sources of waters.
With questing fingers, you ask, 'Beloved Mother, is this where you wish us
to plant our seeds?' You see, for us, planting a garden is an act of prayer, and
we do not take it lightly. We seek the best place for planting by smelling
the rich, perfumed fragrance of Mother Earth, listening to her heartbeat
deep within the soil, and sometimes even tasting the soil to ensure that, yes,
this is the best place to plant our crops. Even in the areas where we, as a
village, have planted for centuries, we still go through this sense of questing
or searching every planting season with the Mother, for we do not take her
for granted.

"I am well aware your farmers in the Human realm cannot plant in the
same place year after year, century after century, for your soil becomes too
tired and can no longer give birth to any crops. Happily, Tír na nÓg is not
like the Human realm, for we treat our Mother with such reverence,
through prayers and with gentle hands, that we do not suffer with the
problem of soil erosion. Because our Mother has taught us the methods we
use, we are able to plant in the same location, the same garden, from millennium to millennium. Therefore, our gardens, like many of us, have
become quite ancient and filled with reverence and a sense of calm stillness.
Our presence in the garden is no more taxing on the Mother than an
autumn leaf gently falling to the forest floor.

"We always use potted seedlings in our planting, since they have had
the chance to grow up feeling protected and safe within pots made out of
heavy leaves. The seedlings are brought out on large wooden carts, which, in
some ways, resemble your wheelbarrows. We gather about these carts and
listen intently for the seedlings to call to us, and they do. The seedlings have
their own sense of consciousness, and they will themselves select the farmer
whom they wish to have act as their midwife. After each seedling has
selected its own particular farmer, we gather the seedlings in their leaf pots
and gently place them into many small pockets that are sewn into the front
of long vests. The vests are brilliantly white to represent Spirit.

"Garbing ourselves in the white vests and picking up our staffs, we
travel to the place of planting. There in the fields, carefully, like gentle
beetles, we bore small holes in the earth with our staffs. Once we attain the
required depth with which both the seedlings and we are content, we ever
so carefully take each seedling out of its leaf pot, ensuring that the protecting, nurturing earth around its root system remains intact. Cupping it

within our hands, we speak a prayer over the small seedling, and then we blow upon it three times—once for the Mother and Father Creator, once for Jesus, and once for Mary. Each plant is thus covered with a blanket of protection, and it is then that, kneeling upon the Mother Earth, we gently ease the small, beloved plant into its new home within the Earth. Singing songs of encouragement, we offer the seedling its first drink of water in what you might refer to as a housewarming gift. The water to nurture these plants is brought out to the fields in small, narrow carts by our assistants, young people who are themselves learning to become farmers. We refer to these carts as wells or, many times, as the Grail Wells. The water held within these vessels is sacred to us, so offering the plant its first drink from a Grail Well is another means of blessing it.

"You may think that it might take quite a long time to plant a garden, and that is true, but, you must remember, there are more farmers than just myself. Though this method of farming may seem tedious to the average Human farmer, we always seem to have a healthy garden, filled to its utmost boundaries and overflowing with healthy crops, so that our Gnome village never goes hungry.

"I will not go into the details of how we harvest our crops, but I will tell you that we gather in our beloved crops with as much reverence as we use in planting the seedlings. Long before the time of harvest, we speak to the plants and sing to them. We tell them about the time of harvest and that they have nothing to fear, for, if they so wish, they will be reborn again in our garden the next season. We sing songs to them throughout the time they grow, and when we gather them and place them gently in our arms, we sing those songs to them once more."

The Gnome village is difficult to see from a distance for their earthen homes are placed among the trees. Low stone walls appear here and there, not to keep out intruders, but for decorative purposes, and they are often used as places to sit and chat with neighbors. The garden is quite large, and it is located in the center of the village in a small clearing within the trees. It is a circular, raised garden, and many varied types of vegetables grow there. The vegetables appear to be of a much greater size than those typically seen in Human gardens.

Ban explained that since Humans tend to grow field after field of the same vegetable, they must do battle with different types of insects or drought and must use various chemicals and fertilizers that are not in harmony with the Great Mother Earth. The Gnome garden is not plagued with such difficulties. No rampaging insects devour the garden, nor does drought weaken the plants, for rain falls gently when it is needed. Still, as part of his duties or function as a priest of the soil, Ban talks to the beings in charge of the rain and requests their help to ensure that the garden will never suffer from thirst. I asked him why, if it naturally rains there often, he would bother to do that. He said it shows respect for the rain beings, for nothing is taken for granted in their realm.

Elowee, Ban's sacred mate, has her own duties in the village, as she explains here. "I have been given the blessed task of teaching the small children of our Gnome Village. I teach them the most important lessons—those of self-awareness and the awareness of all Creation. We help the children to see that every being in Creation is their uncle, their aunt, their grandmother or grandfather, their mother or father, or their brother or sister, no matter whether that being is a cloud in the sky, an old tree in the forest, or a rock next to a spring. We also teach our beloved children to see patterns in all of nature, whether it be a flock of geese flying overhead, frogs croaking in a pond, or leaves falling from the trees. We try to help the children see these mathematical patterns, so that they may have an understanding of what part they play in nature. Obviously, all forms of art are very important to our teaching, for through music, painting, sketching, pottery making, or any other type of art, the children discover their connection and their relationship with Creation.

"They are also taught simple divining skills, such as how to see events by gazing at the movements of clouds or water, and they learn of their Faerie heritage and history through ancient stories. If they are to connect with their natural family, they must also know how to communicate. Therefore, we teach the children the language of the sky, sea, and earth through nursery tales set in song. Though the songs may sound simple to the Human ear, when sung in our language, the child is learning how to speak the language of Creation. Through these songs, the child learns how to speak to all green things, to all stone beings, and to all animals, and this includes the water beings and the sky and wind beings. Though the list could go on and on forever, by the time the children leave their first year in school (or kindergarten), they can have a conversation with any being in Creation."

Willie and Goldie

My relationship with Ban and Elowee continued, and, as I grew to trust them more and more, they began to introduce me to other Gnomes. This was sometimes rather traumatic for me, for my rational mind struggled with the fact that I was seeing Gnomes, beings from fairytales. One evening as I was out in our backyard, I happened to look up and notice a small Gnome sitting on one of the limbs of a maple tree. He wore a red cap similar to Ban's, and great tufts of red hair stuck out from beneath it. He had green eyes, pale skin, and freckles, and he wore a green jacket. What I noticed most about him, however, were the large butterfly wings that grew out from his back and fluttered behind him!

He first introduced himself as Blind Bob, but I later learned he often went by the name of Willie. His jacket appeared to be quite lumpy, and I wondered if he was overweight. He explained to me, in a sweet high voice, that Gnomes often appear pudgy to Humans, because Gnomes like to collect objects like mushrooms, roots, twigs, birds' nests, and stones as they go about their walks. These treasures often fill up their pockets and give them that plump, pudgy look. Willie is blind, and I still find this hard to understand, for how can a Gnome Faery be blind? Still, he told me he can see into our world much more clearly with spirit eyes than a sighted person can see with physical eyes. I was later introduced to his mate, Goldie, whose golden-brown eyes and blonde hair were set off by her lovely blue dress, and to their daughter, Dawn, who has red-blonde hair and golden-brown eyes like her mother. Like Willie, butterfly wings fluttered gracefully behind them both. They would sit together on the tree limbs and watch the sun set or the night sky turn darker.

Here Willie speaks of his life. "Our jobs involve multiple tasks. We hunt among the roots of the trees and along the forest floor for mushrooms, nuts, herbs, and other green things. Humans often refer to the green things as weeds, but we use them for food, healing, and teas. Many times on our searches, we also come upon beautiful stones or leaves or other objects, which we collect and place inside our jackets (or, in Goldie's case, her apron). Even our little Dawn aids us in our collecting with her own small apron. This is why we always seem to have bulging pockets when you see us, because we collect things. We bring them back to the community, so the people can make beautiful objects such as jewelry, decorations for the home, objects to be worn on their person, or even ceremonial objects, often with feathers.

"We have a good rapport with the birds of our realm and others of the feathered Faerie and birds of your realm, and we barter for feathers. Many times, we watch over the feathered ones' eggs when they must be away from their young, so that we may give warning of predators. It is not so much that this is bartering, as we would do this whether the birds shared their feathers or not, but we have a long-term relationship with one another. We give to them, they give to us, and it is a free giving, such as one might find among close, intimately loving families.

"We use our wings to fly up into the trees. Of course, Gnomes also do love to climb trees—that is a Gnome sport and considered great fun. Still, we fly high into the trees and pick fruit that cannot be easily reached, such as apples, pears, cherries, and other whatnots.

"Many times, I and my wife, Goldie, and others of our kind will act as reconnaissance and scout out and talk to the Thunder Dragons and the Cloud Dragons and the Rain Dragons. We try to watch them and discover what they are doing, and we offer requests that an area be watered or an area be spared. In this way, we act many times as ambassadors. I am sorry to say that our requests are not always granted, for the Thunder, Cloud, and Rain Dragons have each been given instructions by Mother and Father Creator to carry out their tasks. We listen to the talk of our constant companions, the birds of the sky, and to the wind itself, for these are also methods of gathering information. Indeed, we gather awareness of our surroundings from the very elements of the air.

"On occasion, we take risks like the Green Cap Gnomes and may actually shape-shift into the form of a bird. There have been legends of us, the magical Faerie birds who sang in the trees and so entranced their listeners that they opened a portal to the Faerie realm. Though some Faerie birds have this capability, we also sometimes shape-shift into your realm as actual birds. When we do this, many times it is to act as a messenger to Humans, who may or may not acknowledge us.

"We choose to shape-shift into this particular form for it is a physical law, if you will, that birds are one of the first creatures to feel the negative effects of trouble in the Human world. In case of a storm, birds are the first to flee. In the event of war, birds are sometimes most quiet and give note that something is amiss. Birds are also the first to suffer the effects of disease or plague or Humans' use of poison gas. This also gives us warning when horrible things are amiss in the Human realm. We are given the blessed ability to quickly leave a realm or shape-shift back into our natural bodies and escape any danger, and we are not at any time in danger, *per se.* That is a gift given to us by the Mother and Father Creator. The worst effect we suffer is the feeling of emotional anguish, or energy disruption if you must put it more technically, that needs to be tended to by one of our healers.

"I must say, all in all, as with anyone you will find in our realm, it is a quite wonderful, free-spirited life, and we of the Faerie realm who are gifted with wings find it exhilarating to fly. We find our greatest joy when we are airborne. Like the small Sprites, we of the Gnomes with wings live in comfortably cozy homes in the treetops and inside the trees. When the females of our tribe are to give birth, they build a nest, but that is not unusual, for all Gnomes who are about to have a child build a nest, whether it is the Gnomes who fly to the treetops or those who live on the ground."

Thurisaz and Brighid

I woke one night to feel a dark shape standing on my side of the bed looking down on me. Now that I had made the initial contact with the Gnomes, and that contact was daily becoming clearer, it appeared that a negative force wished to interfere.

The following evening, as I sat on our screened-in porch facing the backyard, I saw two bright beings appear from out of the darkness of the neighbor's backyard. One was an older Gnome, older in the sense that he had thick, curly, white, white hair, and a long, white beard. His beard was combed into a fork which came down to his waist, and the two front locks of his hair were braided on either side of his head. He strode forward very confidently, and, in his hand, I noticed a thick, wooden staff. Behind him came a younger Gnome with long black hair and a long black beard, also combed into a fork. Like his companion, the two front locks of his hair were braided and came down to his chest. The younger Gnome also held in his hands a thick, wooden staff.

I could tell they were warriors by their mode of dress. Both Gnomes wore black armor consisting of breastplates with attached shoulder plates, while beneath the breastplates were heavy leather tunics with multiple steel rings sewn into the garments for protection against blows or cuts. The long sleeves on the leather and steel ring tunics were tucked into very thick leather forearm and wrist guards. The two warriors also wore white skirts, which came down to just below their knees. Over top of these white skirts were heavy leather and ring skirts, and their feet were clothed in heavy black boots with sharp metal point tips in the toes.

I remember standing there on the porch, watching them approach the screen door, and wondering whether I ought to hastily retreat inside the house. Their presence itself did not seem menacing, but they did walk very purposefully. I was a bit nervous as I observed them moving directly toward me, for they seemed well trained and very confident. There were no jerky or clumsy movements in their gait or in the way they presented themselves, and it appeared from the way they held their staffs that they could use them with lethal force. I hoped they were coming to greet me, and that I was not considered one of their enemies.

When they arrived at the screen door, the older warrior introduced himself to me as Thurisaz. He introduced the younger Gnome as his son, Algiz. In a very strong, baritone voice, Thurisaz stated that he and his son had been sent by the elders to protect us and watch over us, and that we should not fear them, for they were trained warriors and would be willing to lay down their lives for us. I bowed to them, they bowed to me, and then they strode off the porch. Gazing after them as they moved away, I discerned other warrior Gnomes in the backyard. Somewhat bewildered by the evening's events, I retreated back inside the house. It was too much to think on in one night.

Thurisaz and I later developed a close relationship, a close bond, and, though he is a warrior, I also came to know him as an elder. Like Ban and Elowee, he, too, made me an official part of his family and adopted me as his grandson. Here Thurisaz gives a brief description of his life.

"I was first trained as a warrior, and a warrior I will ever be, until that last moment when I take the beautiful forest path to the home of my Mother and Father Creator. That is all I wanted to be when I was a young Gnome—a warrior, to be trained and able to wield a great wooden staff, whirl it about my head and vanquish the evil Ogres and Hobgoblins and others sent by the Evil One. As I grew older, after a few thousand years or so, I realized I had another calling—that of a priest. My training as a priest, as I discovered to my chagrin, was even more difficult than the training I had received as a warrior. It was after several years of training that the robe of priest was placed over my head, and I was given my priest's staff of office. It was then that I realized this calling had filled the void in my life, that certain sense of something I was meant to accomplish. Even though I was a good warrior, a well-trained warrior, there was still something I was missing—some task or some part of me that had not been given birth. It was at the moment I received my priest robes and my staff that I realized I had become whole. It is also where I met my wife, Brighid, for she, too, was a novice, and she was made a priestess.

"Since I became a priest, I have been given the task (and I received it gratefully) of helping initiate the young male Gnomes when they come of age. It is a time when they feel within themselves—and we can see from their aura—that they have come of age. This usually occurs between the ages of eighty-five to ninety years old (which, in Human years, would be similar to being thirteen years of age). The Gnomes are fully grown at that time, at least physically. I help them with their male initiatory rites as they enter (and I use the term loosely here) manhood."

Thurisaz later introduced me to his wife, Brighid. She, like many of the Gnomes, has the face of a lovely, mature woman. It is a face with no wrinkles, and it shows no signs of aging. Her face changes within an instant from the face of an older woman to that of a beautiful young girl, especially when she smiles. Sunlight reflects in her golden hair, which she wears in a braid, as do most of the female Gnomes. Her gentle smile enhances her prominent cheekbones, and her large, brown, slanted eyes give the impression one is gazing into the innocent eyes of a doe. Here she discusses her tasks as a priestess.

"I, like my husband, have also gratefully accepted this duty, and I help initiate the young female Gnomes as they enter womanhood. I am a priestess, and I, too, carry a staff. The rites of initiation for young women are not the same as those for young men. These rites are known only by the female elders who conduct them, just as the rites for the young men are known only by the elders in charge of those rites. The rites have been passed down to them by the elders before them, as have the rites for the young women. We ask the young women and the young men not to divulge what takes place during the rites. I can tell you, and I am sure it is the same with the young men's initiation rites into manhood, that, at the ceremonies, the young ones who are entering adulthood are empowered so they may enter into their new life no longer as children, but as adults with competence.

"The ceremonies themselves lend an aura of mystery. They are not the simple passing of a scroll, combined with the statement, 'Now you are a full grown male or a full grown woman.' Rather, these ceremonies or rites are designed to open the mind gate that leads to the mind well, so these young people may become aware of a new sense of themselves. When the young men or young women first enter the gate of the location where the initiation takes place, they are met there by my beloved Thurisaz, by myself, or by others trained to conduct the ceremony. Before entering the gate, their thought patterns are those of children, and they see themselves still as children. They pass through the gate and enter a forest maze, a labyrinth wherein they encounter mysteries. When they pass out of the final gate, they are no longer children, but, in their hearts and minds, they have become young men or young women.

"The training to conduct this ceremony would be an additional, if you must count it in Human terms, twenty to thirty years added on to our training as priest and priestess. We take this ritual very seriously, for Thurisaz, I, and others trained as we are act as godparents, giving birth to fully-grown adults.

"Thurisaz and I also teach the young music. In some ways, we teach them as Elowee teaches them, but the difference is that usually we teach children whom you would consider in your Human world to be teenagers. We help them select a main instrument, for, by the time they come under our wing, they have tried or possess many instruments. We teach them how to focus on one main instrument and become masters of that instrument. Because they come to us in their late teenage years (in Human terms), they come to know us for several years, and we are seen naturally by them as second parents, so they trust us to help guide them through the ceremonial rites. All who train or who have learned the ceremonies over the labyrinth of new life in some way work with these late teenage children in some field, so that when their time comes to enter adulthood, they will trust them or see them as parents. We believe this is better than having the children go to complete strangers as they pass through this difficult time."

"Like my beloved Brighid," Thurisaz continues, "I teach the young Gnomes music and how to focus on an instrument. We also teach them how to make the instrument of their choice, whether it be a harp, lute, flute, violin, or bodkin. Both Brighid and I, among others, teach them, once they have chosen their instrument, to go out to the Great Mother Earth and actually create the instrument from the very elements. Everything we do has magic in it, so if we wished, we could, of course, have an instrument without the time and focus necessary to create one. However, we tend to make instruments like Humans make them, although the wood and other elements usually come to us as gifts from the Great Mother."

Elfia, Algiz, and Duncan

At first, I did not understand the relationship between Thurisaz and Brighid. I thought they were merely lovers, and I would tease them about their romantic ways. I discovered later, much to my embarrassment, that they were actually married (or mates as they often refer to the relationship). Like Thurisaz, Brighid adopted me as her grandson, though, in truth, she looks too young to be my grandmother. As the relationship developed between myself, Thurisaz and Brighid, I came to know their son, Algiz, somewhat better, and I met Algiz' wife, Elfia, a young Gnome with enchanting hazel eyes and beautiful red hair often held in braids. Ban and Elowee's son, Nigel, later introduced me to Algiz' and Elfia's young son, Duncan, who, like his mother, has red hair, with freckles and green eyes. Here Elfia speaks about her occupation.

"Within our Gnome village, there stands a great hall. It is like our round houses, but much larger, and the outside is earthen. To a Human walking upon it, it would appear as a round mound or grassy hill surrounded by trees, but you would find, as you pass through the doorway and go down the steps, that inside, it is actually much larger and taller. Around the top of this hall are round windows that let in the sunlight. Within the great hall are tall, large candle stands, and we light the hall at night with candles. It is the hall of memories of our people.

"Even when we are still children in the womb, we are continually learning the stories of our people and the others of the Faerie. We greatly enjoy verbally telling the tales word for word and remembering them, and we have managed for many, many thousands of years to lose not one story of our people's history or the other peoples of the Faerie (such as the Elves, Sprites, Centaurs, and others). It is in this great hall that murals are painted on the walls, so that, in some ways, it resembles a Human art gallery. I am one of those who paint new murals of significant events that are happening in our realm, and I make sure the old murals are in good condition. It is not so much that the paint flakes off, though the murals are so old we must sometimes retouch them. It is more that, in our murals, the energies have their own sense of existence, and sometimes they act up, so we might have to retouch an area of the painting. For example, it occasionally happens that the beings in a painting get into a skirmish, since they are to some extent alive. They are not as sentient as all Creation, but they do have their own mental cognizance. I and others keep these murals in good repair.

"All Gnomes have artistic gifts and the ability to draw, paint, and create lifelike images. We all enjoy it to a point, and we use this gift as a hobby. Some of us (and it is not that we necessarily have more talent than others) so much enjoy drawing or capturing images in paint that we make it our lifelong ambition. We are usually spotted at a very young age, perhaps thirty or forty in your Human years. This interest is encouraged until the time we enter training, and this training is similar to an artist's school, where one trains for several years (perhaps twenty of your Human years). No one fails in this school, and no one is denied the opportunity to attend the school if they so wish. Mural drawing always has a place in homes, about our village, in other parts of Faerie, and in the hall of memories.

"When people come through the hall of memories, they already know the stories by heart, and they do not need me to tell them the stories; yet, it is my responsibility to recount the stories to them and tell them what is behind the memories on the wall. We sing them in song or in a lyrical fashion, and, since our own names take two days to tell in Human terms, a mural story could take several days. Because of this, those who come in for a memory song usually come and plan to stay a few days. It is almost like being in the army—some days when Algiz is away on campaign, I may be in the hall singing. We take this responsibility just as seriously as the soldiers take their responsibilities.

"I and the others I work with do not see it as a hardship, but as a joy or a gift, for when you sing of the deeds of your people's past, you reconnect yourself with the families of long ago and the families of the future, and it uplifts your heart and makes you sing inside. It fills my heart cup with joy and helps me reconnect to the Great Mother Earth, to the Creator Mother and Father, and to Jesus by singing these songs. I actually see the spirits of my ancestors, of my grandmother and grandfather, smiling and nodding at me in approval. Remember, time is a circle or a spiral, and when one passes on into the realm beyond ours, one does not die or cease to exist, but still lives on. Sometimes, also, the Elves work in the Gnome library, and the Gnomes work in the Elven library. We know each other's stories, and we may work on a mural or tell a story of our own history or of their history. There has been some discussion of late of establishing a great library, which would contain the works of all the various libraries in one.

"My most important task, however, is that of being a mother to Duncan, our child, with red hair, freckles, green eyes, and his father's chin, though you cannot see Algiz' chin under his long beard. Most male Red Caps have beards, but a few do not grow them, and they are not looked down upon. Once a Gnome does grow a beard, however, then it is considered naughty to peek underneath the beard, so only I am allowed to look under Algiz' beard. They do not usually shave their beards off once they are grown, for, in a Human sense, that would be like walking about without one's pants on."

Algiz now speaks of his duties as a warrior. "In our Gnome community, I am the commander general of the army. I also train the soldiers. Many young men and women come to us, usually when they are one hundred twenty to one hundred forty years of age, to train as soldiers. We help them prepare themselves spiritually, emotionally, mentally, and physically to be soldiers. We wish to ensure they have a good, strong spiritual foundation. I have not yet met a young man or woman who came to us without a strong spiritual foundation, but we change their view, so they begin to look with the eyes of a soldier instead of the eyes of a civilian. Soldier citizens are those who have dedicated themselves to protecting their community, fighting on the side of justice, and defending the good and the just with their very lives.

"The training is ongoing for their term of enlistment. The soldiers may come and go as they please over the years, except during a time of battle or just before a skirmish. Our soldiers are very committed to our army, and so they do not retire from our ranks in mass numbers. I have never seen or heard of a Gnome soldier in our community, or any other village, who left because they were afraid to do battle. Usually they will stay for a certain period of years and then retire, but they cannot decide just before a campaign, oh, I am leaving now. Usually when a soldier citizen decides to leave the army, they so inform the commander (and those commanders would be the captains under me) by scroll and by verbal representation in front of the commander. Usually they will give a notice of one year. They are not held to this year if dire circumstances conflict, and they wish to leave earlier, but that year gives us time to ease their transfer from the life of a soldier citizen to the life of a citizen.

"Training continues throughout each soldier's military life. Basic training consists of how to march, how to use weapons, how the soldier uses things spiritually, and many other areas of training that take a minimum of five years. We all carry swords and staffs, but when a soldier chooses a specific weapon or area of expertise, such as archer or spearman, that training takes an additional five to ten years. They may also choose to become cavalry or foot soldiers.

"You may wonder how we can take so long to train these young ones and still have enough soldiers to fight battles. Generally, the ones who become soldiers (and not everyone becomes a soldier) remain in service for many, many years, and, since new ones come into the service, we never have a shortage. We will not send a raw recruit with less than five years' training out on to the field of battle, except in extreme circumstances when we are being attacked. This has not happened in my lifetime, but it did happen when my father, Thurisaz, was a young man. He was a raw recruit, and they were passing through the various realms to the place where we live now. As they passed through a realm closer to Earth, they were drawn into battle. It was different in those days. Now we send war parties, or companies, into battle in areas that are purposely being manipulated by the Evil One, especially when the conflicts arise from the Evil One's counterparts to us—the Trolls or the Goblins and other creatures. We tend to fight skirmishes with them or others of the dark Faerie.

"During the initial five years of training, the young women are trained by women, and the young men are trained by men. They are not locked up in barracks for five years. They are trained for a series of months, and then they return home to be with their families. After several months of training and depending on the time period, they may be sent home for two or three months and then return for further training. At certain stages of training, they may be home for six months, for we do not feel it is right to separate our soldiers from their families.

"During their training time, we encourage them to learn some sort of skill or side interest, which they will be able to use when they leave the service. They usually begin training in that area after their five years of basic training. These would be skills such as making musical instruments or clothing or an artist might be trained in mural painting. This, of course, continues along with the military training, for, as you know, we do not hurry in anything.

"We help them choose a craft or a skill they can use besides just being a soldier, so they can give to the community. This not only gives them a skill they can use once they leave the army, but also, if we enter an area that has been partially destroyed by invading armies, we may have with us soldiers who are trained as doctors, builders, or mural painters, or who possess other useful skills. Once we build shelter or rebuild an area that has been destroyed, the ones with these other skills can use them to help the community get back on its feet. We are not there just to brandish weapons, but to heal a war-torn area.

"These wars most often take place in realms closer to the Earth, and usually it is because of invading armies of Hobgoblins and Trolls. We drive them out and do our best to repair the damage. It has happened, on occasion, that Hobgoblins and Trolls have turned about from the darkness to the light. They are still Hobgoblins and Trolls, but no darkness is left in them, and they are seen as equals to the Gnomes and others of the Faerie. There have been times when, by the grace of Mother and Father Creator or the grace of Christ, but not by us alone, light pierces through them and drives out the darkness. They find the light, and they change, and they do not change back. Should a Troll or Hobgoblin turn to the light, they are cast out by their own people. Though they still look like Hobgoblins or Trolls, once the darkness has fled from them, they take on a less sinister appearance, and they become trusted allies. Though we do not have troublesome insects in our realms, we do have some of the more beneficial insects, such as bees. Trolls, on the other hand, are troubled by insects, such as large ticks, which are more intelligent than the ticks you would know on Earth. When a Troll turns to the light, he loses his tastiness, and the ticks drop off and go elsewhere.

"The realms the Evil One's forces would invade might include those of the Green Cap Gnomes and Elven realms closer to Earth. We do often go on joint missions with the Elves. We usually bring veteran soldiers with a great deal of experience, and some are trained as cavalry. We have some horses in our realm, but we have many more Unicorns and Winged Horses here, which together make up our cavalry. A group of soldiers you might refer to as the 'air force' ride the Winged Horses, and we do have commanders who use the Winged Horses and the winged Dragons from above. When horses are close to the Earth, they tend to be horses. When they come close to our realm, they tend to grow a horn or wings. The further the realm is from the Earth, the more plentiful the Winged Horses and Unicorns become, especially starting in the middle realms and more so as you go farther from Earth. The animals you see in your earthen realm are also in our realm, but the difference is that they are not hunted in our realm, and so they tend to live in peace. Our spirit Mother Earth realm is the other half of the physical Mother Earth realm, and what one has, so does the other.

"My father held the position I now hold, and, though it is not always passed from father to son, this time it was. Elfia has not been trained as a soldier, and Duncan is still very young. He has been taught by Elfia different instruments now, and he and Nigel are in the same class. [Here we asked Duncan's age in Human years.] We do not understand Human years too well—it seems as though you are here one moment and gone the next. One moment you are a baby, one moment an adult, and the next a pile of dust."

"The position of commander," Elfia added, "was given to my husband because he was best suited for the job. He was the best soldier, and, though his father was very proud of him, that position was given to him not because of the family relationship, but because he was the best soldier, and he was given the honor of that job."

"You understand," Algiz continued, "there have also been female Gnomes who have held this position of commander, for male and female are equal in our service. After the basic training of five years, different instructors, both male and female, teach the men and women soldiers. The male soldiers might be taught by women for two or more years. I cannot tell you how many companies we have, as it would not be appropriate to give out such information, but I will tell you we have ground cavalry, air cavalry, and foot soldiers. The air cavalry is broken up into Winged Horse cavalry and Dragon cavalry. The foot soldiers are broken up into different groups. All soldiers are armed with swords, staffs, and shields. The Gnomes' primary weapon of choice is the staff. Different companies also have archers, and some companies set explosives. They are not as destructive as Human explosives, but more in the line of very powerful fireworks, pretty but dangerous.

"Many of the Dragons breathe fire, while others breathe hurricane force wind gusts. Some Dragons breathe such cold air that ice forms on the enemy, and their teeth chatter, and they fall down. Other Dragons hold large amounts of water in their stomachs and breathe out water on the enemy. They go to ponds, but they can also draw water crystals right out of the air. Some of these Dragons, once they leave our service as soldiers, join the forces of the Elemental Dragons or Thunder Dragons who affect the weather of the Earth. The Water and Ice Dragons are the same type of Dragons, but they specialize. Four types of Dragons serve with our army, but they have five missions—air or wind gusts, water, fire, ice, and the last one, the Earth Dragon. The Earth Dragon physically makes contact with the Great Mother and requests assistance, or calls to her from the air by vocal tones, and the Earth will open and swallow up the enemy in earthquakes. Only the lead Dragons have riders. Dragons are very difficult to bring down, and they are very good soldiers—very obedient—they think in the air (or, in your Human terms, on their feet) very well.

"We do not glorify war and create one for the sheer act of fighting like many of your Human wars. Humans seem to enjoy war for the pure sake of killing. The Humans with whom my father and his father came in contact killed for the pure pleasure of killing one another and us. They romanticized war, as we do in some ways, but we do not take war lightly, for war is a messy business. It is filled with the cries of the wounded and dying, the smell of burning flesh, the terror in the eyes of the victims caught between two warring armies, and the horror and mass destruction of burning buildings. We romanticize the rich tradition of our past soldiers and believe that it is a great gift and honor to defend our loved ones or the weak and the just with our very lives, but we do not romanticize the act of war, for we do not enjoy killing. We do not go on these raiding parties for the sheer joy of fighting. We go there because we have taken an oath to try to help others who are less fortunate than we are.

"These skirmishes happen often, and, especially in the last fifty years of your Human time frame, the skirmishes in the realms closest to your Earth have become more frequent. Mild skirmishes happen almost daily now, but many ones that are more dangerous occur as well. We understand they will be picking up even more, for they reflect what is happening on the physical Mother Earth. We do it to protect the Mother Earth and Humans and because of an oath we have made to the Spirit Mother Earth out of love for our Mother.

"I like being a soldier, a warrior, a commander. I like the feel of armor on my body, a shield at my side, and a stout staff or sword in my hand. I like the feel under me of the Winged Horse upon which I ride, the strength and power of the Unicorn, or the incomprehensible power one feels upon the back of a Dragon."

CHAPTER III

Henry and Gwladys

My wife was very curious about my conversations with the Fair Folk. She realized I could not remember or write fast enough to retain all that was said, so she offered to become a scribe. Weekly question, answer, and conversation sessions between the ever-growing group of Gnomes and us soon became a regular event. This was later christened the "Gathering of the Grove," and the talks eventually increased in frequency to several times a week. My wife asked far too many esoteric questions, and I had to stretch my understanding farther and farther to grasp the complex words and pictures presented to me during these gatherings.

I noticed that a very beautiful Gnome with glimmering white hair and large brown eyes usually led the Gathering of the Grove. The lovely face of Gwladys, like all the female Gnomes, is ageless. Though she is an elder, at a moment's notice, her face can assume the appearance of a very young maiden. She usually stands or sits before us at the Gathering and holds in her hand, as do all Gnome elders, her large wooden staff of office. By her side stands her husband, Henry, also an elder of the Grove. Henry is a traditional Gnome who takes great pride in wearing his red cap, even when it must be exchanged for a red nightcap when he retires for the night. His red cap barely contains his thick thatch of salt and pepper hair, and his brown eyes usually hold a twinkle of mischief or a jest waiting to pop out. His long, bushy (but carefully combed) beard, which is of the same salt and pepper coloring as his hair, falls to his waist in a curling point, but it cannot conceal his all-encompassing, welcoming smile. Henry told us the following story of how he came to become Gwladys' sacred mate.

The Story of Henry's Quest

"As you both know, I am a trained priest, as is my beloved Gwladys. I knew her before we took training together. When she was a little girl Gnome, not too long ago, I used to watch her as she would play with her friends around the roots of the great trees. She and her young friends would set up their little households among the trees' roots. The great trees I am referring to are much taller and have more massive trunks than the trees in your earthen realm. The great roots of the trees as they rise up above the ground appear to be almost wooden caves. Gwladys and her friends would set up little homes and pretend to be doctors, artists, and warriors, and they would come home to their caves at night and greet their husbands. Because they were children, most of their husbands were invisible.

"As I watched this fair-haired beauty play with her friends, even as a little boy, I fell madly in love with her. I wanted to join her and her other friends, so I gathered up some of my little boy friends, and I returned to the scene. After working up my courage, I asked if we could play with them. Gnome children are more sociable than Human children are. They rarely say, 'You cannot play with us because you are boys,' or 'We cannot play with you because you are girls.' They welcomed us. Gwladys was pretending to be an Elven queen, and she needed a captain of the guard, a royal servant to attend to her every need, and that was I. One moment I was the captain of her guard and fighting off evil Trolls and Ogres, and the next I was her foot servant, following her around and carrying her crown made of flowers. She knew, even as a little girl, that I was madly in love with her, but she still made me make mud pies and eat them."

"Well, I was a little girl," put in Gwladys, "and our mud is healthier than that in your physical realm, with no harmful elements in it. I treat him much better now; I don't make him eat mud pies."

"She would also make me be her cook," Henry continued. "That was another of my titles, so I would make these mud pies for her, and she would make me eat them. Now, as a Human boy, I would have gotten very sick, but, though the mud did not harm me, even in our spirit realm, mud is not that tasty. I would rather have had other things, like a bowl of cream or vegetables or a real pie. Then, one day, I had the glorious duty of being her horse, so I had to carry her about. In fact, all the boys suddenly were horses, and we had to carry these royal ladies or little girls on horseback. We had to take them to the forest on their daily rides.

"As we got older, I thought Gwladys secretly liked me, but she would not tell me that. The game began to change, and I became a prince, as well as being the royal foot servant, soldier, cook, and horse, so I knew she liked me a little, because I went from being those other things to a prince who was courting her. As a prince, I had to perform noble deeds to win her favor, and they were impossible tasks. I was a little bit older at the time. I was probably shy of being a teenager in Human years, and I had written many poetic songs to her and sung them."

"They were quite beautiful songs, too," added Gwladys, "but, being a young lady entering what Humans would refer to as my teenage years, I could not tear myself away from my reflection in the water. During my reflection gazing, I decided that I needed a feather from the Eagle who rests on the top limbs of the Great Tree that sits in the center of the Sacred Grove. This was the first task I set for Henry.

"Now resting upon the floor of the ocean lies a massive Clam. Within this large Clam is a perfect pearl. The pearl is a true object, but it is also a symbolic object used sometimes in our spiritual meditations. That was Henry's second task—to retrieve the pearl of wisdom from the mighty Clam. This Clam has never surrendered its pearl to anyone, for it is meant to keep the pearl and only release it on the day the spirit Great Mother Earth merges with the physical Great Mother Earth in the eyes of the Humans (though she has really done this already).

"The third task I set for Henry involved another true being, but also a symbolic one. There, at the gates of the pathway that leads into the Mother and Father Creator's realm, rest two great golden Lions. They are not there to block or bar the way to the Holy Parents' realm, but they are there to ask you questions. You converse with him or her (male or female), and they will help you decide if you are ready to enter the realm or not. By conversing with them, you may realize you are ready to pass through the gates, or you may decide to turn back and wait until a later time. They are somewhat like totems or spirit animal guides. I requested that Henry bring me back three golden whiskers from the female golden Lion and three whiskers from the male golden Lion, so I might braid them to wear in my hair."

"My first task," Henry took up the story again, "was to retrieve a golden feather from the Golden Eagle who sits in the uppermost limbs of the Great Tree. I began to climb the Tree. At first, the going was easy, for the way the roots grow out from the Tree, it is like a natural stairway, and up I climbed. Even the ridges in the Tree made climbing easy. Though we are Faerie and immortal, we are still bound by some rules in our realm, and so I realized, as I went higher and higher, that I was not getting any closer. I had begun climbing with the sunrise, and the evening sun was now setting, and I had not even begun to reach the top of the Tree. I was much higher than many Gnomes had traveled before by climbing, and I was quite high up. I could see the torches of people below me as they gathered for rituals and praying.

They were very tiny below me, but I was nowhere near the top, and I was tired. It appeared the higher I climbed, the taller the Tree grew. And though we can travel anywhere in our realm by taking the special forest pathways, it would not be acceptable at all to take a pathway to the top of the Tree, and no one of the Faerie would ever do that.

"I began my climbing again early the next morning with the sunrise. Higher and higher and higher, I climbed. All day I climbed, until evening when I rested again, but now my food supplies were gone. During the second evening, I lay there bemoaning that fact and talking to the Creator Mother and Father and talking to Mary and Christ, saying, 'Cannot you put me on the top limb or just give me a golden feather?' At that time, a Squirrel had traveled down to where I was, and he asked me what I was doing in the Tree so high. I told the Squirrel I was there to get a golden feather from the Golden Eagle on the top limb, and I asked him if he would bring a feather down. The Squirrel told me I was being foolish, and that one would never get a golden feather away from the Golden Eagle without asking permission first. Then I asked the Squirrel if he would run up there and ask the Golden Eagle for me, but the Squirrel told me he himself had never been to the top. He had been very high in the limbs, but never to the top, for if he were to travel to the top, he, as a Squirrel, would pass into the next realm, and he was not ready to do that. I asked him to do the best he could, and he volun-teered to go up as high as he could. Then he would call out to Squirrels higher in the Tree to pass on the message (Squirrel yodeling, if you like), and this is what he did.

"It was during the middle of the third day that I sat on a thin limb, totally miserable, half on and half off, hanging limply like a rag. I thought that perhaps if I hung there like that, feeling very sorry for myself, the Great Mother and Father Creator would take pity on me, hanging so miserably like a dishrag, moaning and groaning and looking as pathetic as I could. It was then that I heard the beating of wings. It sounded like the beating of Dragon wings, and it was so massive a sound that I had to clutch the limb to keep from being blown off. I thought, what was this, a Dragon flying near me? Our Dragons are peaceful and friendly, but one still needs to show them respect. I looked up then and saw the massive Golden Eagle. He said he had received the message from a Squirrel who was in the spirit realm. This Eagle has the ability to travel into our realm and into the realm of the Mother and Father Creator at will. I told the Eagle of the quest I had been sent on by my beloved, and I pleaded with him to give me a feather. I must admit I was afraid he, too, would send me on a quest. He looked at me from side to side. Then he literally plucked out a feather and gave it to me.

"He said, 'My mate also sent me on many quests before we were mated,' and then he took me on his back and dove down with me to the ground."

"Henry," said Gwladys proudly, "is the only non-priest Gnome in such a circumstance to ever receive a golden feather directly from the Eagle. The Eagles do, on occasion, give feathers to the priests for ceremonial reasons; however, Henry was at that time a young boy and not a priest."

"Gwladys said," Henry continued, "Do not come back until you have fulfilled all the quests.' The next quest was the quest for the pearl of the sacred Clam. I had taken a small curran out as far as I could into the ocean, and, though I tried to take enough supplies, the boat was small. I could have traveled there, of course, on one of the spirit pathways, but on such a quest, it would have been considered cheating or impolite to do that. If you sent me on a quest today and told me you needed me to travel to the other side of our spirit realm and collect a certain item there, and I agreed to do it and not to take the pathways, I would be gone for a very long time, at least in Human years.

"I sat in this boat, though I did not need to, for a day, becoming quite sun-baked. Then out of the water rose a great water Dragon who towered over my boat, and he wanted to know what I was doing out in this small boat so far from shore. He wondered why I had not used other means to get out there, like a flying horse, or a bird, or a magical boat, instead of taking this old leaf boat. I told him of the quest of my beloved, and I told him I had received a golden feather from the Golden Eagle. The Dragon looked at me for a moment, and I heard him begin to snigger. His lips began to quiver, and he laughed and laughed and laughed, and then water began to shoot out of his mouth. He was almost like a fountain, and the water made my boat go under water for a short time.

"He noticed and pulled me out of the water. Soaking wet, I asked, 'Will you talk to the great Clam, so I may have the pearl of wisdom?'

"He replied, 'Foolish child, you know the great Clam can never give up its pearl of wisdom until the physical and spirit Earth merge as one in front of the Humans, for the birth of Christ and the birth of the golden age.' He laughed some more, drenching me again with water, and then he said, 'You will never get the pearl from the Clam, for to do so would cause spiritual chaos.' The Clam itself, you see, is a gateway within the ocean to the Holy Parents.

"'What will I do?' I asked. 'She will never, ever be satisfied with just a golden feather from the Golden Eagle.' I don't think the Dragon even believed I had it to begin with."

Here Gwladys interjected, "I would have been very satisfied with the golden feather, and that would have been the end of it."

Henry continued, "The Dragon held me in his claws and brought me back to shore. He took one of his scales, which gleamed like a pearl, and said, 'Give her this. Perhaps she will be satisfied with this.'

"I had a golden feather from the Golden Eagle and a gleaming scale from a water Dragon, and I had but one quest left. I began my journey to the outer realms, taking the sacred paths from which none return. Now, you remember, none will take these paths unless they are ready to move to another realm. If one takes these pathways, they know within themselves it is time for them to move on, and they are greeted by the golden Lions when they reach the gateway of the Mother and Father Creator's realm.

"I was walking these pathways, which I should not have been on, for in my heart I was not being called there. As I passed through these pathways in the forest, a Bluebird watched me from her nest. She could look at me and tell, for she had watched many pilgrims walk these pathways, that I was not ready to be there. She flew down, alighted on my shoulder, and said, 'Why are you walking these pathways? You would be welcome, young one, but you are not ready to walk these pathways yet.'

"I told the Bluebird of my quest for my beloved and my first two adventures. Unfortunately, I do not believe the Bluebird believed me, for, being a bird herself, she could not believe the Golden Eagle would give me a golden feather, and I did not carry it with me, for I did not wish to lose it. Neither did she believe I would sail out into the middle of the ocean, for no boy in his right mind would ever do such a thing. I told the little Bluebird that I was going to walk the path to go on the quest for my beloved. Seeing that I was quite determined, she flew off in search of the two Lions, for she, as all birds, can fly into the realm of the Mother and Father Creator and back into our realm. She told the Lions that I was coming down the path.

"A very short time after my conversation with the Bluebird, I rounded a corner, and there, sitting in the middle of the path, was the male Lion with his much-needed whiskers bristling at me. I told the Lion of my two adventures, and that I needed three whiskers from him and three whiskers from his mate to make a hair band for my beloved.

"I first thought he was roaring at me, but he was actually roaring with laughter, and he laughed for quite a long time. He said, 'My beloved child, we cannot give you our whiskers, for we cherish them greatly. To pull them out causes undue pain, and we cannot part with them.' Then he added, 'For if I and my mate each pulled three whiskers out of our face, our faces would be lopsided.' He was talking to a boy, and he was teasing me.

"Then he said, 'I will give you six hairs from my mane, and that will have to do for a hair band,' and he gave me six long hairs from his mane. He believed me and believed my adventures; he saw they were true! Then he made me climb on his back, and he ran back to the area of pathways where I could go home on my own. He said I was not ready to come back there for a long, long time, and when I did come, my beloved would be with me."

"I had missed him," said Gwladys, "as it had been over a week since I saw him last. I thought he had given up on me, and I was quite forlorn. I sat on a tree root and mourned his passing, for I did not know he had taken me seriously. I saw him striding up to me with a cautious smile on his face. He was beaming, but he was nervous, and he had three objects wrapped in fine samite. He put the three parcels down at my feet, and he asked me to open one parcel first. I unwrapped it and found the diamond-like scale from the water dragon. It glimmered and shone in the sun, and it was blinding. It was as though I was holding a star or the sun in my hand. He said he could not get the pearl of wisdom, though he had tried, but the Water Dragon had given this to him and brought him back to shore. He said he was sorry he could not get the pearl of wisdom, and he looked very, very sad.

"Then I saw the six golden hairs from the golden Lion's mane, and I almost fainted, for he had traveled the path, and I feared he could have been lost. Henry said the Lions would not part with the three whiskers from each, as it would make them lopsided, and they would fall over. But the male Lion had given six hairs from his mane, and he hoped that would make a good hair band for me. I was close to tears, for he had risked his life for me. He thought I was very sad he had not brought back either the pearl or the whiskers.

"He asked me to open the last parcel, and I saw the golden feather from the Golden Eagle. He told me he had not climbed to the top of the Great Tree, for he had grown too tired, but the Squirrel messengers had carried the message, and the Eagle had come down and given him a feather. I realized he had risked much, and I began to cry even harder. He thought I was very unhappy, for he saw me as the girl who stared at her reflection in the pond. Then I embraced him and hugged him and began kissing him on his face, and I thought he would run away, he was so shocked. It was from this moment that we said verbally, though we had known it before, that we would be mates, and it was after our teenage years, after our initiation as young adults, that we became wedded or married.

"I still have the Dragon scale, which I often wear as a necklace about my neck. I still have the golden hair band, which I wear in my hair. And I still have the golden feather, which rests on a plaque above the fireplace in our home. Henry is the only one of the Faerie given a golden feather for courage alone, so, of course, I had to be his mate. This is how we met and realized we were soul mates. He does not ever have to prove himself to me again."

Henry's Fine, Magical Cloak

Now it was Gwladys turn to tell her story. "As Henry is the illustrator of books, I am a writer of books. I write mostly books concerning our history, our folktales, or memory tales of our ancestors, and Henry illustrates them for me. Anyone in our society can write if they wish to become writers, and all of us, Gnome and Elven, have written before, whether it be poems or stories. Many of us have books in the library, and Merlin and Lili have written several books that can be found there. You could say I have become known for my writing, but I am not so much a celebrity as some of your Human writers. In our realm, everyone is a celebrity in his or her own way.

"I began collecting stories as a young toddler from my grandparents and their grandparents and their grandparents. It is possible, you see, for us to have living great grandparents many times removed. We are in no danger of losing our history or heritage or stories, but it is always good to tell the stories in a fresh light for new understanding. You may wish to tell the stories I share with you in the future, but you will also add your own seeds and life to them, and they will continue to grow and be remembered. Many of these stories have disappeared completely from the Human realm, although many of the stories involved or influenced Humans directly. This is the story of my gift for Henry after I was presented with the three marvelous objects he had worked so hard to bring me.

"I wished to return to Henry a gift for his generosity and his bravery, so I decided to make him a magical cloak. I decided Henry's magical cloak would be so fine that its fabric and fit when he wore it would be so pleasing to the eye that it would only bring out the finest points of his bearing. He would look taller and more handsome, his eyes would sparkle more, and his voice would sound more golden. It would give him inspiration, only wisdom-filled words would pour from his mouth, and others would think what a fine Gnome he was. It was not that the cloak would cast a spell of glamour around him. Instead, it would enhance the fine qualities he already had, for, even though he was young, I felt he would be in a leadership position.

"In the art of spinning, an object like a comb, which is called a card, is sometimes used to help comb out the fine thread so it can be combined with the other thread. There was a certain large Boar in our kingdom who had once thought a card such as this could be used to comb out the hairs on his back, so they would all become the same thickness and would not become tangled. This was what the Boar first thought, but, unfortunately, the card had become caught in the hair on his back, and it had not worked out at all the way he had wished it. I believed that once I had been able to hold in my hand this card that had been caught within the hair of a very wise, very old, and very magical Boar, that using the card to comb my wool and make the fibers all fine would cause the properties of this Boar to be woven into the fine wool strands. You see, not only was this Boar very old, very wise, and very magical, but he was also the leader among all Boars, and he was the king of all boardom.

"Now this king Boar had all these wonderful traits, but he also had one particularly nasty trait, and that was that he was the most cranky, ill-mannered, destructive Boar that had ever run through our realm. He would run through the forest very impolitely. For instance, people would be out in a nice meadow having a lovely picnic when suddenly this huge, cranky Boar would come charging through their picnic. Disrupting everything, he would trail their picnic cloth behind him and drop it several miles further down the way, usually in some pond or puddle. The Boar does this as a spiritual duty, for he is filled with light, and it is his purpose, given to him by the Holy Parents.

"So I decided I must have this card at all costs, and I set about to get it, unknown to my family, my parents, my grandparents, and unknown to my Henry who would have told me not to do it. I knew that the great Boar drank from a certain watering hole every morning before he began his rampage of running through the forest. I hid behind some bushes in the trees, waiting for him to come down for his early morning drink. He arrived, as large as a Unicorn, with tusks that curled up in front and over his head and curled back upon themselves, somewhat like ram horns. He would use these tusks to carry away objects or, sometimes, to push Gnomes out of the way or to butt unsuspecting Unicorns from behind and knock them out of the way. Sometimes he used it to teach the lesson that, when you hear charging hoofs coming from behind and things being thrown out of the way, you should look behind you, and move out of the way.

"He was drinking water, and I heard grumbling noises in his stomach and grunting and growling. As those scary noises were being emitted from him, I became somewhat frightened and thought of turning back, for usually only warriors would take on such a large beast. I thought perhaps he was so ill mannered because no one had ever taken the tack of being polite to him, since they were usually shaking their fists or yelling at him. I thought I might win his good humor and accomplish my task of getting the card from him by being polite, so I came out of the bushes.

"I was very nervous and trembling, and I addressed him, 'Lord Boar, a comb is trapped within the hair on your back . . . if I may borrow that?' Then he raised his great snout at me and charged me.

"I stood there, not sure what to do. I think I must have stepped partly out of the way, for suddenly I was flying and landed on his back, which made him even angrier. Off we charged through the woods and through the meadow, with me clinging onto his back, screaming all the way. I must have ridden his back for hours, all through the morning, through the forest, over hills, under trees as he tried to knock me off, into streams where he tried to drown me, up steep hills, down steep hills. We disrupted a few picnics, and he even took me through the Gnome village. Then, when the shock wore off our little Gnome village, he had a troop of Gnomes chasing after him, trying to get me off his back. Being a spiritual, magical being, however, he was faster than the Gnomes were.

"I finally stopped screaming, for I became hoarse. After a time, as I tried to grip his hair, which had become quite slick from wallowing in the mud puddles and from sweat, I began to clutch the card itself. Early morning turned into late morning, then early afternoon, then early evening, and, finally, late night. We went to places I had never seen before, and he must have circled back, for I could see the Gnome community with lights out, searching for me. I also heard Elven voices, Centaurs, and others of the Faerie. The comb I was gripping moved farther and farther back, until I was finally riding upon his rump, and then I fell off with a whump into the leaves.

"The Boar turned around and came to me and stood glaring down at me with his large, baleful eyes. His snout alone was larger than I was. In a large rumbling voice, he spoke to me, 'Ages ago, I took that card to try to comb out my fur, so it would become fine and soft and all the same, and as I pulled, it became trapped and stuck within my fur. The more it was stuck, the angrier I became. You have pulled the card from my hair and have made the hair on my back all the same thickness, and for that I give you my thanks and the comb.'

"He ordered me to climb once more upon his back, and he took me to the village, within sight of the others, and he let me off his back. Then, with a snort that sounded more like laughter, he disappeared into the trees to become a questing beast and a spirit guide for some other hapless victim in the future. I wrapped the wool about the comb to make it the same thickness, and, with the wool I ran through the card, I wove Henry's cloak. It is a fine, magical cloak that to this day enhances all those wonderful qualities within my beloved and brings them to the forefront, so everyone can see what a wonderful man, husband, and priest he is and what a blessing from the Holy Parents.

"From the time we are babies or very young children, we are taught the folktales of our ancestors, of their encounters with magical beings and magical animals who sent them on quests and helped them grow spiritually. The reason we know our folktales are true is that, as we grow older, we experience the same magical adventures our ancestors did. We ourselves encounter magical animals and magical beings who help us grow spiritually. In our realm, it is not considered fantasy for one to encounter a magical Boar, a talking Salmon, a magical Hart, a shape-shifting Eagle, or some other magical being. We do not believe that the person who has these experiences makes them up, for we all have had such encounters. It is a shame that Human religions have taken such magical encounters out of Human consciousness and closed the gates to such possibilities; in our realm, this is how we grow spiritually. It seems in the Human realm that if one has such experiences with magical spirit animals or magical beings, whether they be ill-mannered Boars or beautiful Angels with great wings, one is often ridiculed by other Humans in the community, and so they close the gates to a great potential for spiritual growth.

"My beloved Henry's and my own main task is to act as a priest and priestess for our community. In our roles as priest and priestess, we lead the ceremonies. We also act as advisors to those in our community, and many times, we act as advisors to visiting dignitaries. We even travel to other communities, such as Elven and other Faerie communities, and counsel kings and queens. When I say we, I mean not just Henry and myself, but also the other priests and priestesses of our community, for others besides ourselves act in these roles as priests and priestesses. We are taught and reminded, even to this day, that, though we have this honored duty as a priest or priestess and though we counsel others, we also receive counsel from our own people. Our role is no greater than, nor are we elevated above, others in our community, no matter who they are. It is a very honored and sacred task, and no priest or priestess takes it lightly. We must strive to keep our spirits pure and uncluttered, that we may become good, clear, pure vessels for the blessings and the knowledge of the Holy Parents and for their counsel, that we may share it with the people.

"At times, we also travel into other realms closer to your Earth to act as negotiators or mediators between warring factions. I am glad to say that many Gnome priests and priestesses are asked to do this, for those of the Faerie closer to the earthen realms do not see us as a threat or hold the fear that we have ulterior motives. You may say they see us as being quite harmless, though, as you can tell from our warriors, that is not always the case, for when needed we are great fighters. We are called upon many times by those of the Elven in the realms closer to Earth, for they feel we will be fair and neutral negotiators, who will strive to bring the mantle of peace between two warring, angry factions. The closer one comes to Earth or the earthen realms, the more anger you may experience between parties.

"We also go to these realms closer to the Earth to act with the doctors and assist them in their healings. Though the doctors are better trained to heal energies, we are better trained to heal spirit, so we travel with them to these realms to be a comforting support to those ravished by war or other difficulties. Granted, most wars we have seen that last for hundreds or thousands of years have been not among the Faerie themselves, but among the Faerie, Trolls, Goblins, and Ogres. Thousands of years earlier, we were sent to try to negotiate peace and settle hostilities between the Elven and the warring Humans before the time the Elves pulled back further to realms more distant from the physical Earth.

"For over four thousand years, Gnome priests and priestesses have trained side-by-side with Elven priests and priestesses. Therefore, we come from the same school, and both of our peoples strive to be pure holy vessels. That is why we are called Holy Mothers and Holy Fathers. Gnome priests and priestesses are not greater than Elven priests and priestesses and *vice versa*. We are of an equal caliber, but each of us is an individual in our spirituality. In many cases, though Elven priests and priestesses are called in, we are called in also to settle disputes. In all negotiations, we are asked to accompany the Elven priests and priestesses, not because the Elven priests and priestesses are less spiritually pure and not because they do not try to be clear channels for the Holy Parents and for Christ and Mary, but because many of the skirmishes involve the Elven. Therefore, it is better to have non-Elven priests and priestesses to provide a sense of impartiality, so the fear that their loyalties will lie more with one side than the other does not become an issue.

"For instance, in the ancient days when the Humans were waging war on the Elven realms closest to the physical realm, the Humans distrusted Elven priests and priestesses, though they would be just as impartial as the Gnome priest or priestess. However, when a Gnome went into the field, the Humans would grudgingly give their trust or authority to hear the counsel of the Gnome priest or priestess, and they would accept their counsel. This was due to the fact the Gnomes were not related by direct blood to their enemies. Likewise, in more recent skirmishes between those of the dark Faerie (Hobgoblins, Ogres, and others), even the dark Faerie would trust the judgment and counsel of a Gnome priest or priestess before they would trust the counsel of an Elven priest or priestess, for they believe that the judgment of the Elven would be in favor of their own people. This is quite understandable, though, in actuality, the Elven priestesses and priests would be just as impartial as the Gnome priests and priestesses.

"The realms closer to Earth are in the most danger at present. Were they to be viewed as tree rings, the outer rings would be the Human realms, and here would be where most of the wars are taking place. Most are being fought by Elven against the dark Faerie. The Elven and other Faerie who are not dark Faerie would not even consider taking the life of one like themselves, a Faery of light. They actually refer to themselves sometimes as the Children of the Light. Perhaps the only disagreements you might have between the Children of the Light would be minor disagreements, such as over a deed of land, and even these are quite rare. The realms closer to the

Earth are larger and more massive than the Earth, but the Elven tend to live close together. Though they have much room to spread out, and though the land within these realms is unlimited (unlike in your Human realm), the Faerie in those realms do not always see it so. In some ways, they are living in an illusion that their space is limited, and that they cannot spread out. Therefore, living closer together, disagreements about deeds of land sometimes occur, though they could quite well pick-up and move farther out from each other. To be honest, though, in the realms closest to Earth, you also have the dark Faerie living in groups or clusters, and perhaps they live closer to each other for protection. Therefore, because of living so close to each other (though by Human standards it would be considered living far apart), land becomes important to them. In your Human realm, unlike any of the other realms, you truly are limited in physical land space and the gifts, or what you refer to as resources, of the Great Mother.

"The battles being fought in the realms closest to Earth by the Elven are mostly against the dark Faerie or against the occasional incursion by Humans, such as travelers or shamans, including government-trained ones. These Humans go there to try to claim or bring back a token of their shamanic or traveler prowess, usually spirit objects to increase the power of the shamans or travelers, or to use these Elven realms to travel to other realms. Some Humans enter these realms closer to the Earth to make deals with the dark Faerie. Some of the groups who practice what they consider the Old Ways do, in fact, make pacts or agreements with the dark Faerie. They perhaps refer to them as demons or dark guides in an attempt to cause these dark ones to do their bidding. They believe they gain the upper hand over them, and that the dark ones become their slaves, but this is not true. The dark Faerie may appear to do their bidding for a time, but the Humans will learn that they will be the ones to become slaves, for how can Humans bargain successfully with beings who may be thousands of years old? Demons also exist, but these are other beings entirely, which we do not wish to discuss at all.

"The further you travel in the realms away from the Human realm, the more darkness burns away from your spirit. Those who are truly dark cannot survive the journey. The realms closer to the Earth are mostly taken up with darker beings, but those who have more light than dark can travel farther and farther into the realms. Most of the Elves live in realms farther from Earth. Your Human realm itself is not surrounded by darkness, for pathways of light cut through the darkness and cannot be subdued. Your earthen realm is not alone. Were we to draw a map using the rings as found in a tree, it would be only an image, for you must understand that our realm is closer to you than your own breath. The presence of the Holy Parents, Jesus, and Mary is even closer to you than our own realm. It is the beat of your heart and lies between the very heartbeats themselves."

Chapter IV

Esther and Jürgen

During one of our gatherings, the possibility of Gnome doctors assisting my wife with energy healing sessions was discussed, and it was decided that they would help. The two healers who first introduced themselves were Esther and Jürgen. Esther is a young, female Gnome with long red hair, compassionate green eyes, and a warm, friendly smile. Her husband, Jürgen, has eyes of a clear blue and usually wears the traditional Gnome red cap over his blonde hair. Though he has no mustache, a rounded, blonde beard encircles his chin. While Esther has a thick Welsh accent, Jürgen was the first Gnome I encountered with a Germanic accent not of the British Isles. Here Esther talks of their healing work.

"Jürgen and I are Gnome healers for our little community. We work primarily with the energy levels of the beings in Faerie and sometimes those outside of Faerie who have had their energy or their spirit damaged by outside forces. We do work with physical matter to some extent, but, as doctors, we believe that if you heal the spirit first, the body, in most cases, will follow. In dealing with physical bodies, the time comes when all bodies must return to the womb of the Great Mother. In such cases, though the spirit may be healed, the body does not follow, and, instead, becomes once again a part of the Great Mother. Most of our patients are Gnomes or Elves who need their spirit energy healed due to prolonged contact with Humans or manmade objects, or due to pollution or other materials that cause a wound or tear in their energy field. They come to us, and we heal their spirit from the inside out. Many Green Caps, or the Gnomes we refer to as front-line Gnomes, have more direct Human contact (though Humans are unaware of it). They spend more time in your elements, and so they suffer greater spirit damage as they go about their duties of working with the plant and animal life and other children of the Great Mother Earth.

"We also work in accord with Elven healers, for they, too, suffer some damage during their contact with your Human realm. Again, it is not the Great Mother's physical body in this realm or her children, such as the animals, rocks, and trees, that cause this damage. It is not just the air quality and the prolonged Human contact in the form of man-made structures or carriages or vehicles. It is also the actual man-made energies that fly through your air and bombard the entire physical world at a constant rate on a continual, non-stop basis that cause harm.

"It surprises us that Humans live as long as they do with all the negative influences you are exposed to, not only through pollution in the air, but also in your water and the very food you grow and the food you eat, whether it be vegetables or meat products. It fascinates us that many Humans who are beginning to take on what they consider to be healthier lifestyles, in that they 'eat right' or exercise, yet seem to find other ways to poison themselves. They become more involved with their machinery and the poison energy it emits, such as that which comes from computers, telephones, televisions, and even the automobiles you drive.

"The method for Humans to become healthier is, of course, to eat right, exercise, and get plenty of rest, but also to heal the spirit. They seem to leave out the spirit many times, and not many Humans know how to heal the spirit along with the physical body. When I speak of the physical body, I am also speaking of the mind where you would find your Human emo- tions. As you know, negative Human emotions will literally act as a cancer or corrosive substance in your mind and physical body and your spirit, and so many Humans become ill and perish before their time or lead a life that is quite miserable."

Jürgen here describes his first meeting with Esther. "Esther and I have been practicing medicine together for quite a long time. If you must know, in the Human time frame, I would say (if we round up the years) perhaps thirty-seven hundred years. Before we met, we were both young doctors in our own practice in different parts of the Great Mother's spirit realm, the realm we inhabit now. We met one another at what you would refer to as a convention, but which we refer to as a gathering of a medical grove, which is held once a year in mid-May. A larger one is held every hundred years, and that is usually attended by healers from all the realms, even the realms closer to the Earth, and from our own realm. It was at one of the smaller medical gatherings that I noticed Esther. She was one of the doctors from a village that, by your Earthen reckoning of distances, is very far away. Were you to use a typical Human means of travel, it would take literally years to reach her village. Due to our forest pathways, we are, of course, able to travel such distances within moments. As you can tell by my accent, in our realm (or the spirit Mother Earth that reflects the physical Mother Earth), I was from a Gnome Bavarian village, so I had come with a colleague of mine to this medical gathering.

"We had entered a great circular clearing in the grove, and I had taken my place in a pile of golden leaves with my friend. Far, far in the front of the clearing before all of us was the speaker, who was giving a lecture on the spiritual shock suffered by many of the Green Cap Gnomes due to their prolonged contact with the Human realm. Though she was quite a distance from me (perhaps two kilometers, for it was a large clearing), I was able to see her bright red hair and her lovely face. Instantly, I fell in love with her. I could not focus on her lecture. I just remember standing up and waving my arms frantically, trying to get her attention. Now you may not realize that we Gnomes and others of the Faerie have the ability to cause our voices to carry great distances by a sort of singing chant or shout. It is a mixture of the two, similar to yodeling, and, in the middle of this lovely creature's lecture, I was determined, through this chanting shouting, to get her attention, thereby disrupting the entire lecture, which was filled with several thousand Gnomes. Since I had caught her attention and the attention of the entire gathering, she asked me, again by our method of chanting shout, what was my question? I realized, to my horror, that I had no question, for I did not know what she was talking about. I tried very hard to remember the words she had been speaking, but I could not remember a thing.

"I did the only thing I could and stilled my heart, braced my feet into the comforting warmth of the Great Mother, and asked her if she would be willing to have dinner with me after the lecture. There was stunned silence for a time, for no one remembered her speaking about dinner during her lecture, but because we Gnomes have a very good sense of humor, laughter began, and, though she was a wee bit embarrassed, she consented to have dinner with me. I thought she consented to have dinner if for no other reason than to give me a poke in the nose."

"I have to admit," said Esther, "I was quite taken aback and a little embarrassed, and I thought, was he not listening to my lecture at all? But he was, and, as you know, we Gnomes and Elves have rather keen eyesight, and I saw he was quite attractive, this rash Bavarian Gnome. I consented to have dinner with him if for nothing else than to meet a Gnome brave enough to stop me in the middle of my lecture and ask me for a date. To be honest, I did not know if he was very brave or a rogue or a mixture of the two, but I am happy to report to you that he is very brave. I discovered that, and I also discovered he is quite a rogue. After our first evening, he sang to me. He had taken notes of the lecture and made a poem of them, and he sang them back to me, commenting on how lovely I was. He made a very beautiful poem about me."

"I commented on her loveliness," said Jürgen, "and her enchanting voice and on how knowledgeable she was on the subject. It was a love poem mixed in with a review of her lecture."

"I must admit," continued Esther, "no one had ever sung me a love poem combined with a medical lecture before. It is hard for you to understand, I am sure, but it was quite enchanting, and we fell in love. For a time, Jürgen and I traveled to the front lines, for we saw that the need was greatest for the Green Cap Gnomes. Though they had their own doctors, many of us of the Red Caps and Elven healers and others of the Faerie volunteered to go to the front lines to treat the Green Caps. Even in that period (about thirty-seven hundred years ago when we became mated or married), Humans were invading territories of the Faerie, especially the Elven, and our services and skills were needed there as well. For a time, the Elves whose bodies were more physical were literally suffering plague from contact with the raiding Humans, and they were also suffering injuries brought on them by the weapons used by the Humans.

"We also began to treat Humans during that time period, on the battlefield. Sometimes they did not make it back into their own realms, and we treated them. The Elven will not kill a wounded enemy, even the most hated one. They would nurse them back to health, and then send them on their way. Sometimes they would befuddle the Humans and send them deeper into other realms without weapons, hoping they would learn to live more peacefully away from their warlike culture, so we would treat those Humans. In many ways, we were like your Peace Corps, young and idealistic. Now we are older, but still idealistic, and we feel quite blessed to be healers.

"The training to be a healer usually is seventy-five years and then twenty-five years as an apprentice before you become a doctor. We are still considered young Gnomes, but there is really no definite time period for being considered old. There is 'young' in our society, but there really is no 'old'. When the time comes for a Gnome to move into the further realm of the Mother and Father Creator, they take the forest path, and they move on, but it is not because of their body breaking down or physically dying."

Charlie and Renie

As we were introduced to more and more Gnomes, I became a bit overwhelmed by the growing number of new faces that regularly appeared at our Grove Gatherings. Trying to match names with faces became quite a challenge, but, even when I could not remember a name or recall a face and would wither in embarrassment, the Gnomes would merely laugh it off and happily tell me their names and share their stories with me again. It was during one of my strolls through a nearby park during my lunch hour that I noticed a Gnome walking parallel with me in the woods. For a time, he just smiled and nodded at me, and then he approached.

I was somewhat startled to see he was not wearing a red cap as so many of the Gnomes did. On his head, instead, was a shorter, rounder cap, green in color, which helped contain his wild, curly, black hair. His friendly brown eyes were so dark that they appeared almost black. He introduced himself to me as Charlie and told me he was named after a famous English king, who had passed his mother on the road just before his birth. Charlie informed me he was of the Green Cap tribe or community, and that the Red Caps lived in a realm far removed from the Earth, in what they refer to as the Garden, while the Green Caps had taken on the grave task of caring for the physical greenery of Mother Earth.

As my relationship with Charlie grew, I was introduced to his wife, Renie. Like her husband, Renie wears a green cap, which covers her long, brown hair, which she sometimes braids and other times wears loose with only a smaller braid. Her modest smile complements the sometimes-shy look in her soft, brown eyes. I later learned that Charlie and Renie are elders of their small community. Shortly after meeting them, I learned they were soon to become parents, and, after a time, Renie gave birth to a baby daughter, who was given the name of Bonnie. Bonnie has grown into a beautiful young girl with golden-blonde hair and hazel eyes. Charlie speaks here of what life is like for a Green Cap Gnome.

"As you can tell, I am a Gnome of the Green Cap tribe, and our job is to provide support, nurturing, and counseling to the Faerie closer to the front realm and also to the Great Mother and her children. This translates into all green things and rocks and even Humans when they listen to us. I was trained by my Grandda when I was a very little lad. He had already been doing it for thousands and thousands of years, and, by the way, he is still alive. He was ancient when I was born, and now he lives in semi-retirement in the realms farther in. He has earned that rest, I think, and, maybe, in a few hundred more years, he will make that trip to the Holy Mother and Father. We do not see it as death, for he can come back if he wishes. He is just going home to be with his Mum and Da.

"Anyway, he used to take me along with him when I was a wee lad, barely able to walk, I think, for I would trip over my shoes a lot. We do not put shoes that fit exactly on our children when they are toddlers; we put on shoes that are ever a little bit larger, maybe up to a half-size bigger. You are wondering why would we do that—because we like to watch our children fall on their faces? No, we make the shoe a half-size larger with the expectation the child will grow into it. Then, when the child grows into that, we make it another half size larger, and we continue to do this over and over. It acts as a blessing for the child, so that the child will always have bigger shoes to grow into. Though this may sound discomforting, it really is not. We are quite good shoemakers, and, of course, you may have heard a few legends about us. This ever-larger shoe fitting continues until the child becomes a young woman or a young man Gnome. It continues for probably eighty to one hundred years, for it is when their feet stop growing that they are considered grown-ups. It is sort of a passage of initiation into adulthood. When they become adults, they are given shoes that fit their feet. This is our culture, our tradition, and we know it is silly. Believe it or not, wearing large shoes for the greater part of your young life allows you to learn to move fast through tight spots when you are spotted by Humans. Imagine, then, when you have shoes that fit how much more limber and fleet of foot you become.

"I was a wee lad, and I was barely out of toddler shoes and walking about, and I had stuffed some acorns in the space between my toes and the tips of my shoes. I was walking about, tripping over roots, and falling down, and I was laughing, and my Grandda was laughing, for, unlike Human children, we do not get bruised when we fall. That is lucky for us, because we fall a lot as children. My Grandda began to teach me that day the ways to care for those we meet along the path.

"I am a healer, not so much like the doctors, but I go in along the pathway more into your physical realms. There I encounter plants and animals that are in distress, and most are in distress now, I am sad to say. I lay my hands on them and offer energy for them to escape the condition they are in at the time. When I travel outside the park area, I lay my hands on those about to die and travel to the spirit world. These include animals that are hurt or dying due to Human intervention, or sometimes intervention from other animals, and the trees about to be cut down. I sit with them for a long time, sometimes until their death, and I help their spirit enter the next realm. If they are filled with enough light, I bring them to the realm where the Red Caps dwell.

"It was hard with my Grandda that day, for we came across a mother bunny and her children, and she was dying. She had been struck by a stone arrowhead from a young Indian lad who had been practicing his archery skills. He was out looking for her, and her children were not safe. She was outside her burrow trying to lead the young boy away from her children. We sat with her until the lad found her, and we helped ease her spirit out of the body, so she would be gone by the time he arrived with his other boy companions. I remember I was crying a lot, and Grandda had tears in his eyes. The Indian lad was filled with light, and he was doing what he was supposed to do. They had to eat meat in those days, though perhaps it is not so necessary now. If your machines stopped working, and you were to go back to the old ways, you would have to eat meat again, unless you all became farmers, and I do not see you doing that, not unless you must.

"Then the mother bunny was gone from her body, and she watched us as we eased the spirits out of her children and brought them over to the other side. We could not leave them behind, as they would die without their mother. That was my first experience with death in your world. I did not fall down so much that day, as I was walking with my head down, sadly thinking about what had happened.

"Every day is not about death. Sometimes you encourage a small sapling to grow and not to give up. Sometimes you will talk to an old tree that has stood there for hundreds of years and listen to the thoughts he or she may have to share. Sometimes you listen to stones and hear what they experi- enced that day or over the past thousands or millions of years. Sometimes you talk to animals to see what is going on, who is preying on whom, who is hurt, who is not, who has had babies, who is pregnant, or who is going into heat. Many times, the conversation drifts to Humans.

"The Humans in those days that you refer to as Indians could see us pretty well. Sometimes they would not, but it was not too hard to make them see us. My Grandda confronted the boy holding the mother bunny that day. As the boy held her in his hands, Grandda told him to give thanks for her life and to be sure to use all of her, so her death would not be for nothing. He told the young boy never to kill an animal unless he had to do it for food to survive. He did not try to talk the boy out of eating animals or tell him to eat only vegetables or acorns or leaves. Humans in those times needed meat to survive. I know you have an argument that they could have become vegetarians, but it was not in them, and it is not in Humans today, though their bodies would be in better shape for it, and they would live longer, too, and it would be kind to the animals.

"Green things suffer, too, when they are about to perish or die or give up their lives. It is easier in some ways for them, for they know that this is part of their mission in life. The animals know this, too, but the green things always had a bit easier of a time. Still, to them, their life is very sacred, and they want to live. You see, the green things have many different tribes; yet, in reality, they belong to one massive tribe. I guess you would call it the tribe of the green things, but they have many different chieftains and chieftesses among these tribes. I could sit here and talk about the oak tribe and the willow tribe and this mushroom or that mushroom tribe, but, pretty much, they are all under one higher leader who you would refer to as a Deva.

"Now, believe it or not, the Humans and animals are part of the same tribe. Understand that when I say the green things have their tribe, as the Humans and animals have their own tribes, it does not mean they are not related. Two tribes may be hundreds or thousands of miles away from each other, but they are still related to each other. Therefore, you Humans are in the same tribe as the other animals, the same tribe to which we Gnomes belong. Humans and animals, especially mammals, belong to the same tribe. If you studied the teachings of the Indians, you learned that a long time ago, but now it must pass from your brain to your heart.

"I learned pretty much everything about being a scout. Grandda dealt mostly with the animal situation, and my Grandma was good at speaking to roots, berries, trees, mushrooms, and the falling leaves. Come fall time, leaves are the ones who need the most counseling. They turn golden and the most beautiful they have ever been, and then they die; they fall to the earth. Most leaves know that is their job, and they are fine with it, and they come back anyway. Grandma would walk among the leaves, sing to them, and remind them they would come back next spring in little green buds.

"Green Cap Gnomes usually take on the jobs their parents have had and most of us do pretty much the same things, *per se*. We tend or minister to the needs of all Creation in the physical realm, helping those in the spirit realm and helping those closer to the physical Mother and Father. However, most of our ministering deals with the physical, for here is where the battle is being waged, and this where the most casualties are found.

"It is not always a sad task, though, for we dwell out in the middle of Creation, and we hear the songs of the birds and the gossip of the crows and the wind as it sings through the leaves. We hear all the old stories, the trees know our names and call to us, and we have chats. I guess it would be like walking through a Human neighborhood so lovely that it makes the heart ache with joy. Everyone on the street knows you and calls out to you, and the day never gets gloomy or sad. Well, actually, the gloomy or sad part is there a lot in the physical realm, because of what we see happen to nature, but the rest of what I said earlier is right, and that is how we see our job. I use the word 'job,' but it is not really a job. It is a part of life. It is like living or taking a breath or the beat of our hearts. That is not a job; it is life.

"We Green Caps have our doctors and our healers. Also, many Elven and Red Cap Gnomes and others of the Faerie come to help heal us, for we do sometimes take sickness upon us. It is the sickness of our spirit from seeing so much sadness in your physical realm. When this happens, we take a sabbatical that sometimes lasts months and sometimes years. Though I now work within an area you refer to as a state park, many years ago, in the beginning of the industrial age, I saw what was coming. I saw the darkened skies and the men working like slaves in the factories, and I became heart-sick. I retreated into the realms closer to the Holy Parents for a time, I and Renie. It was only with the birth of the park some years ago that I came back, so I took quite a long leave, you might say, in Human terms.

"So that is about it—that is all I do. Oh, we do have people who make our clothing, and I am speaking about among the Green Caps, though all the Faerie trade among themselves. This may be stereotypical, but the best makers of shoes for the Faerie are the Green Cap Gnomes. You have legends about us behind bushes—the tapping of the hammer. You Humans call us leprechauns. I am a leprechaun, but I am really a Gnome. A leprechaun is an Irish Gnome. If Humans could see or hear us more clearly, they would hear the tap, tap, tap of our hammer as we make shoes.

"You may wonder, since I am a leprechaun, whether I might have a pot of gold. I must admit we do like shiny things, but most of those pots of gold we did have were stolen by Humans. What do coins mean to us? We trade in acorns, nuts, roots, and herbs. We barter. What does gold mean to us? We make our own jewelry, but what we wear is made from spirit metal that is more pure in form. If I had a pot of gold, since you caught me a long time ago, I would share it with you. If I come across one or find a friend who does, I will ask them if they want to share it with you.

"When we do have gold, it is not because of greed. We are like crows. We like shiny things and history, something to hang on to. We are a bit like the Dragons who amassed large amounts of gold and jewels. Some of those Dragons did tend to become greedy, and it did transform them, although not many Dragons did this, I am happy to say. It is like having a pretty thing in your house, and you come home one day, and it is gone. It is quite a sad thing. I must say that, just because a Human caught one of us, and he had a pot of gold, it does not mean we all have pots of gold. For the longest time, Humans would chase us about looking for a pot of gold, and we would say, we do not have a pot of gold, go away, but they would chase us still. I hope whoever spread that rumor tripped over their shoes and skinned their knee, but that they lived to grow old and fill many shoes.

"For those few of us who do have pots of gold, we sometimes make energy copies of the gold. It is as though the object we take is giving birth to its twin, a twin in every way, and it does not take away from the original object. When we would have a bag or a pot of gold (the extreme few of us who do), we would reach into it with our hands. With the energy from the pot, we would form a second or a twin, and we would use that second pot of gold to make our jewelry. The good thing is that if we used up all the gold from the pot we had copied, we could always go back to the original pot and make more gold. We do not like to make a twin from a twin; we would rather return and make another copy from the original. That is why you might find some Gnomes to be rather protective of what they have. They were also afraid Humans would use it to put up a bunch more buildings, cut down more trees, and be even ruder than ever before.

"Now what am I trying to get you to remember? Very few of us have a pot of gold. No one in the park has a pot of gold. Those who might have a pot of gold would be Green Caps who could have stumbled across it as they were working on the physical Earth. With all the hard work we do, if a Gnome stumbles across a pot of gold, that Gnome deserves it. I know you are thinking that, if we found a pot of gold, we would behave like some Humans, becoming greedy misers and just sitting there with our pot of gold, never going anywhere. That is not really true, for it becomes rather boring, and gold cannot talk to you. The few who stumble across such a pot may make a twin of it and never come back to it again.

"Let me say, for all Green Caps here and for all shoemakers and those considered leprechauns, very few of us have pots of gold, so leave us alone. Well, come talk to us and ask us about the weather, but do not ask us for pots of gold. We will just give you a few twigs. There have been stories of Humans who chased leprechauns about and threatened to drown them or smack their head against a tree. If someone were doing that to you, of course, you would take him or her to your treasure, and, while that person was digging it up, you would disappear. The treasure, however, was usually nuts and roots, which *was* our treasure, but the Humans would say, oh, the gold was transformed into those nuts and roots. They would grow bored, and leave us alone, and then we would have our treasure again.

"But, you know, this was before my memory. There have been some stories in the Holy Isle of Ireland that have happened more recently. Those people in Ireland, those of the Celtic blood, and those even of the blood of your native people, your Indians, or people close to the land—it is easier for them to see us, and perhaps we have had some run-ins with them. Unfortunately, we are in the front lines dealing directly with Humanity. We are not like the Red Caps who long ago passed away from the reach of Humans, so the stories could be true. I am happy to say, though, that my relatives have no direct stories of being chased about by Humans trying to find our treasure. My treasure is life itself. My treasure is my wife, Renie, and my daughter, Bonnie, and they are treasures I am giving up to no one, Humans or anyone else. You two have become part of my treasure, too, and I will be leading no Human over to you.

"So, to finish up, besides making shoes, many of us are clothing makers and instrument makers. All the Faerie are very good craftspeople, but sometimes an Elven will come to us for special shoes or instruments, and sometimes we will go to the Elven, perhaps for a new jacket or a hat. So that is about it, my life is pretty simple . . . for a poor man. Please put that in several times."

CHAPTER V

Rebecca and Lorithoth

Through Charlie, I came to meet other Green Cap elders such as Lorithoth and his wife, Rebecca. Rebecca's eyes are hazel, and she usually wears her long, silver hair loose, with small braids in the front locks. Her husband, Lorithoth, has gray hair, a long gray beard, and friendly, hazel eyes. Here Rebecca explains how they create musical instruments.

"My husband and I have a small shop where we make and design musical instruments. We produce many of the old traditional instruments, such as the lute, the harp, bagpipes, and smaller Irish bagpipes. We also create more of the modern instruments you have today, such as the guitar. The mandolin and even the violin are rather modern to us, since we have been around for many thousands of years. Gnomes and Elves both come to our shop to barter for our instruments, and we do have a bit of fame and recognition, for we take great care in selecting the wood for the instruments. We try to ensure that much love, craftsmanship, and magical ability is placed in each instrument. We bless the instrument, so it may produce only the clearest sounds it can make. Like the Grail, it becomes a pure vessel, one that will emit only beautiful musical tones. For the one who uses our instrument, the musician who bonds with it and makes it his or her own, we put small blessings, so that the musician's skills may increase, and they may lead a blessed life and become the best musician they can be.

"It is true all of us at one time make our own instrument, beginning from the very first process of going out to the forest and selecting the great branches of wood the trees have left behind or given to us for our use. Still, a place exists for people like my husband and me. You see, some of us are artists as far as painting or drawing or the crafting of shoes or clothing. Others may be the builders of homes or the makers of tools or shields or swords or jewelry. Yet makers of musical instruments are also needed. I know you may be thinking that if you make your own instrument, you will bond with that instrument. That is true, of course, but sometimes you meet a stranger in a crowd or you see someone coming from afar. You feel as though you have known them forever, and they become your closest friend or your beloved mate. Though you still love the ones you grew up with and were close to, you bond with this new person and begin to create a life together. That is how it is with a musical instrument. All of us at one time make our own instrument from scratch, for that is the basic training of all Gnomes and Elves. These lessons are taught in the early years of schooling, but there can come along, as you pass through life, another musical instrument that bonds with you and becomes like family to you. It is an instrument that was made for you, but is not always made by your own hands. That is why we have a thriving business.

"In the early morning, when most Humans are still sleeping, my husband and I go out into the woods just when the sun begins to wake up and shed his first beams of light within the forest. We walk through the trees, more in early morning darkness than in light, and we say our little prayers greeting the day and thanking the Holy Parents and Christ and Mary for the gift of life and the trees for sharing with us. Because our eyesight is good even in the early morning darkness, we will spot a shape here or there or a branch here or there. By looking at it, if we take our time, we may see an instrument lying hidden within the gnarled and twisted limbs. Of course, we do not make a decision right on the spot. Instead, we collect limbs of different types of wood, such as maple, oak, and spruce, and we load them on a small cart. When the cart becomes full, we bring it back to our shop. We let the limbs sit about our shop for a period of time, sometimes for years, for we have enough to do, enough instruments to work on, that we do not need to hurry.

"Eventually, Lorithoth and I, like sculptors carving an image out of marble or clay, carve here and there, shape here and there, feeling with our fingers, looking with our eyes, touching with our heart, and sensing the instrument that lies hidden within. We never force the wood to bend to our will or to become the instrument we desire it to become, but we let it speak to our hearts and eyes and the touch of our hands. They always tell us what they want to be—a drum here, a harp there, or perhaps a violin; it is their choice. After we shape and construct the body of the instrument and carve designs into it, we may paint the instrument or coat it with protective covering, much like the paint or varnish Humans use.

"We work with the instruments and bless them until they shine like the brightness of the moon's face or the blinding rays of the sun. Like moonbeams on a pond at night or sunlight passing through the leaves of the trees and forming patterns of light and shadow on the ground, the instruments take on their own lives and actually hum. We listen to the stringed instruments before we string them, for we can hear the sound of the music they will play in the future. As we string them and tune them, our fingers caress them as a mother would the face of a newborn child until we have the right tone. Perhaps we may play just a few songs to make sure they are tuned right and are at their best. Then we set them aside, for it is not for us to play them, but for the ones who will come after us with whom the instruments wish to share their lives. An instrument never really belongs to anyone. It shares its life with you, but, if it is ignored, it will turn its back on you like a rejected loved one. Its music will be silent, and the room and your life will be the emptier for it.

"The drum skins we use are made of great leaves, which we cover with a special coating, so they do not break when we tighten them around the frames. The leaves of some of the great trees here are quite large, and when they turn golden with the coming of autumn and fall to earth, we collect them. From one leaf, we can make several drums. We already hear the sound of the drumming before we stretch the skins, like a heartbeat, an ocean wave, the thump of a spirit staff, and the silent musings of the Great Mother Earth herself. Then we tighten the leaves onto the rim. We always make the drumstick from the same limb, so that they will never be parted. Then we begin to drum, and our small shop begins to shake. The Great Mother begins to dance beneath our feet, and the heartbeat of the Holy Parents is heard throughout our village. It is joined by the clapping of hands, the strings of other instruments, the stamping of staffs, and the slap of bare feet on the Earth. We tend to do this at a certain time of the week, so all may expect it. It may turn into a feast, even, that begins at early mid-afternoon and ends in the wee hours of the morning.

"We make many instruments, but we never try to make more than are needed or requested, for many times we act as babysitters for these instruments, reassuring them that their music mates will come and retrieve them. We stroke their painted wood and lightly touch their painted surfaces, and, as Lorithoth and I go to sleep, we can hear the slight murmurings in our shop, as they gently play and lead us to sleep."

Lorithoth continues here, speaking of their tasks as elders. "You may have noticed, as my wife has spoken, that we become the very parents who give birth to these instruments. They depart from their life as the limb of a tree, becoming separated from their parents, the tree itself, and pass into what may be considered death by Humans, but which is merely a transformation or rebirth into a new life. This life is just as beautiful as when the instrument was still a limb upon a tree, when the wind would pass through the leafy branches, singing a song and rocking the limb gently with its voice.

"We do consider ourselves blessed parents, for we do not have a Gnome child of our own. There are not many of us, but some of us choose not to have children. This is not because we cannot, or are told not to, or even that we make a conscious choice. It just happens this way. It is the Holy Parents' plan, we believe, so we can put our focus on our instruments. They become like our children, and, though they may travel to distant realms far from our small shop in the village, we can still hear them while standing outside our shop. Their gentle whisperings and their soft voices are carried to us from great distances by the beloved wind. They tell us they have not forgotten us, that they will always remember our touch, and that ours were the first faces they saw when they were born as musical instruments. It is not as though Rebecca and I are abandoned parents; instead, our children always come to call on us, their musical notes carried by the wind.

"Another of our tasks is to act as priests or elders for our small Green Cap community. Green Caps are the front line caretakers for the plants in your Human realm and in the realms nearest to the Earth. We were tempted to follow the Red Caps into the distant realms, but we could not bear to part completely with the green life here in your realm and the face of the Great Mother. After counseling with the Red Caps, who had themselves considered returning or remaining in this Human realm, we understood our destinies were different, and they were to pass further into the distant realms. In many ways, they would be the pioneers in the spiritual awakening, and they would be there for support when others, such as the Centaurs and Elves, followed in their wake. We, the Green Caps and the Red Caps, are part of one family. Though we are separated by many realms, we have not lost our ties with the Red Caps, for distance means nothing to us, since we can travel great distances in moments. We are within a realm that is close, very close, to the Earthen realm, but it is protected in such a way that it is as spiritually pure as the realm the Red Caps and the Elven live in. It is a gift to us from the Holy Parents. It provides us with a place to rest and to heal, so that, on a continual daily basis, we may enter within breaths or heartbeats of Humans.

"We pass among you unnoticed and work to heal the plants, the vege-tation, all green life, and trees. We help to work and heal all animal life and even the Great Mother's own physical face and what you refer to as the earth and the rocks themselves. We also respect and work with the different, but very small, groups of Humans who work with us knowingly or unaware. We stand by them, help them, and commune with them, hoping that they may have full consciousness with us, although they rarely do. These groups are very small and do not cover the face of the Great Mother. They are made up of peoples like the Hopi and other original inhabitants of this land and other lands who still strive to maintain the memory of the Garden. These small groups are becoming even smaller and are in danger of vanishing; yet it is by their efforts and their work in communion with us that the physical face of the Great Mother and all physical, animal, plant, and rock life does not perish and cease to exist, and the Great Mother's physical presence, her body, does not become an empty, dead husk.

"You see, we feel we have been given a great task by the Holy Parents and Christ and Mary. Though the armies of Humankind are against us, we must strive to do our best, for it is a matter of life and death that we suc-ceed. When I refer to armies, I do not refer only to your physical soldiers, but to your large merchants (your companies) and the physical holdings they have and to other greedy devourers of the Great Mother, who threaten to steal her very breath, so they may build up their treasuries with more jewels and coins. They are like the legends of the dark Dragons you hear from time to time. These dark Dragons do exist in the land of Trolls and Goblins and dark Elves. For thousands of years, they amassed the great treasures of Humans and those Faeries who left behind, or were chased away from, their treasures. The dark Dragons would pile them into a large heap and sit upon them, not that they could use them or purchase anything of use or value from them, but so they could keep the glitter to themselves and keep a tally of every bauble or trinket, so that none might be stolen or lost. Those hapless victims who took a small trinket, even to feed their family or to keep themselves alive, would be scorched by the wrath of these dark Dragon merchants. Your merchants are not like the elemental Dragons, who may cause healing and sustain life through what might first appear as destruction. No, your merchants are more like the dark Dragons, the hoarders, who steal life itself, so they may count their treasures and soften their bed of greed.

"Now, to retrace our steps back to our original discussion, we act as counselors and elders and priests and priestesses, mainly to others of our Green Cap community, though we have also counseled and led ceremonies for others of the Faerie as well. Along with leading ceremonies, we find ourselves counseling very weary or frustrated Green Caps, whose energy levels are quite low. They fall into a condition you Humans refer to as depression. It is unheard of for a Gnome to remain in a depression for a long period of time. Therefore, we are needed in the front lines for counsel and support, to be a shoulder to weep on, to give encouragement and hope, and, if need be, to physically carry them to safer realms or transport them to Gnome or Elven doctors for healing. You could say more of our priests, priestesses, and doctors come to the Human realm than come to other Faerie realms, for the battle is great, and many are wounded. This is the area where the largest number of Gnomes are wounded or made heartsick. This is where most of our work as counselors or elders takes place, and this is also where most of the doctoring work takes place. If a Green Cap is so wounded or their energy so low they begin to fall into depression, they are carried or transported by us into a safe realm, or to our realm, where they recover over a period of several days.

"Once Green Caps enter the Human realm, they may dwell there for a period of weeks in small camps. Because the camps are in spirit form, a Human may pass by one and not even notice it. It is not as though the Green Caps have fixed tours of duty. They stay for a period of perhaps a month in Human time, if that long, and that is usually a Green Cap family—a husband and wife and their children even—and after a time, they return to a safe realm, maybe even a Red Cap realm. There they may dwell, perhaps for several months, until they are renewed and ready to venture to your realm again. Fortunately, there are many of us, so we constantly rotate troops who physically work with the Great Mother Earth.

"When we come to the Earth realm, it is like settling in a vast land where occasionally you may run into circumstances or beings that will cause you distress. You may be able to dwell in this land for quite some time before you have difficulties, but, at some time, you will. The little communities we form in your Human realm are, by Human standards, quite peaceful, much more peaceful than your streets outside. Humans, however, cause us distress by their acts of filling the air with pollution, noise, or fumes; throwing their discarded items and trash on the ground; harming small animals or even one another; harming trees or any green thing; and even by carelessly kicking a rock out of the way. The stress these actions cause is filtered through our communities. The machines inside and outside your homes throw energies through your homes that are not helpful to you. Even if you were to turn off your computer or television, you would still have energies flooding your home, and this energy eventually causes stress to the Green Caps who dwell in your realm. This is why they usually need counseling from priests and priestesses like ourselves or need medical contact; it is not due to physical contact with Humans or other beings.

"We do have help from Elven priests and priestesses and doctors and other beings of the Faerie, who help us and support us. Many times, the Centaurs help transport us from the Human realm if our families become too weak and despondent to carry themselves. Even in the Human realm, the Green Caps are looked after by Mother Goddess and Father God. Our home realm is much like the Red Cap realm, unreachable except by paths provided by the Holy Parents, unbreachable by any being that is dark. However, we do find it our task or our mission, to leave the safety of that realm and venture into the Human-held realm to work with others to keep the very physical face of the Great Mother alive."

The Devas

Having heard mention of Devas from other sources, we asked Lorithoth and Rebecca to help us understand the Devas' place in Creation. Rebecca began to explain this to us.

"You have asked how we work with Devas. You must look past the learning you had as children and past the doctrine you have been taught. In many ways, the Devas are similar to the Angels, except that Angels usually dwell in the Holy Parents' realm, except for the Guardian Angels, who dwell with all the children of Creation. You can compare the Devas to the Guardian Angels who protect each of you, for they dwell mostly on Earth, but travel back and forth to the Holy Parents. Your Guardian Angels dwell in close proximity to you and could be at your side as quickly as your breath to protect you, unless otherwise instructed by the Holy Parents. Now Devas are very similar, except that they tend to protect an area instead of a person. Some protect an area and some protect groupings, perhaps the Deva of squirrels or the Deva of a certain type of plant or the Deva of an area. A Deva is in many ways similar to the Lady of the Lake, the position Niamh holds now and which Lili once held. Niamh protects a certain sacred area. All areas are sacred, so all areas will have a Deva protecting them.

"As the reflection of the Holy Parents, the Deva also has a male mate. As the Lady of the Lake always has a Lord of the Land, so does a Deva. While the Deva heals, protects, and nurtures, so does the Lord of the Land. He prowls about the area, working more as a front line warrior. Human words do not express this properly. It is as though he takes his staff and walks the area, no matter how small or large, and tries to ensure its protection. He tries to access those who enter the area and instill in them a sense of sacredness for the area, so they may take care of the area. Unfortunately, Humans have become so separated from spirit that they rarely hear the Lord's warnings or the Lady's concerns, for Human ears and eyes are often deaf and blind to spirit.

"Because of this, many Devas require attention also, from counselors or elders such as us, and medical attention, but, unlike us, they do not leave their area in the physical Mother Earth until that area is overcome or destroyed. They remain there, and, many times, with the help of others of the Faerie, we must lift them on a litter and carry them out. They never die, but they can become very sick, tired, and sad and sometimes take years to recover, for they refuse to give ground or give an inch until an area is over-come. Within your cities, think how many Lords or Ladies were overcome. Some try to stay on, even with the mass destruction of the land, and though homes now stand where trees once stood. They try to instill in Humans a sense of sacredness, and they try to bring peace to this land. Sometimes they succeed, for if one is passing through an area, one does not usually pay attention, but if one dwells in an area for a period of time, such as in a home, one tends to recognize the sacredness of the place or at least become subconsciously aware of it. With a sense of compromise, more at the loss of the Devas, an uneasy treaty is set into place.

"The Devas can sometimes dwell in an area, and that place becomes peaceful. At other times, however, they become overwhelmed by the dwell-ers on the land and what has been done to the land, especially in the pres-ence of a merchant building. They are overcome and taken to a place of rest where they can recuperate. Another Deva and Lord usually arrive then, knowing full well what is there, but having accepted their fate to maintain the land until it is liberated or until the original Deva and Lord return. They come even to a merchant building, and they dwell there, merely holding the land until it is once again liberated.

"The Devas almost always return to their chosen land. They watch the ground, and if they see a leaf or a weed or a sprig push its way through the blacktop of a parking lot, then they rejoice that even one has made it. They know there will come a day when the land will become liberated once more, that Humans will once again live in harmony with all nature, all Creation, for though Humans are the greatest transgressors and assault the Great Mother's body, they are still loved and cherished by us. We call out to you as family and ask that you hear us, and stop the abuse of the Great Mother and the walling off of yourself and your children. We hope that day will come soon."

True Tom

Since we have spoken here of the Devas, this seems the proper time to introduce you to one of the Tree People, though we ourselves did not actually meet him until several years later.

Through the art of far sight, or seeing into other dimensions, we find True Tom standing among the trees of the forest. He can appear as a man over six feet in height or as a very tall and ancient tree. His hair is dark and shaggy, and a great, thickly twisted beard flows down the front of his chest almost to his waist. Clothed in medieval attire, True Tom is a very powerfully built man. Within his hair and beard can be seen the leaves of many different trees, not woven in, but growing as a living part of him. For this time and place, he has chosen to be known as True Tom. He likes the word "True" before his name, for he is always true in his speaking and is one who abhors lies. Tom has been one of his names for quite a long, long, long time. He tells me of the jest he has made of the letters, "T" for tree, "O" for or, and "M" for man, for he is both tree and man, ever shape-shifting from man back to tree and from tree to man.

"Is it my turn to speak yet?" Tom asks. "You have heard aright. My name does be True Tom. I was gifted that name long ago by my Mum in ages long forgotten. Perhaps the name was not exactly Tom, but Tom is close enough for me today. I hold to this name as a way for others to know me, just as an oak holds to the name 'Oak,' and a birch holds to the name 'Birch,' and a willow holds to the name 'Willow.' It may not be our true name, but it is how people know us. It is more of a nickname to me. It is true, also, that I am both tree and man, though I prefer the shape of a tree. To be honest with thee, I think I was born a tree first, and a man after, for I have always known the ways of trees, but the ways of men to this day still confuse me.

"I have floated in and out of your realms, in and out of your Human history, for some time. I give you a wink now and tell you that a Human man spoke to me not too long ago about ages past and long departed, but which I remember well. The days we spoke of were one of the last times when Men and Elves fought side by side together in your physical world. Those times be long gone now, but that evil monster we fought against, though defeated, appears to have been reborn in your age. Perhaps Elves and Men, Gnomes, and others of the Faerie kingdom will once again join together in a vast army to stand up against the great evil.

"I have witnessed much evil during my long, long, immortal life. I knew well the tree that later became the cross for Jesus. The tree held him up, filled with part grief and part reverence that it had been chosen to hold his tortured body. This tree was willing to give up its body, its spirit, for Jesus, who was willing to give up his life for all Creation. I, True Tom, see that you have lost your way once again. You are like sheep that, when the shepherd steps away for just a moment, wander off and become lost by themselves. With your sheep's foolishness, you wander right into the fangs of the wolves. Though my words seem harsh, I do not mean to pummel you with them. That is not my true task in this small space in which I have been allotted time to speak. Nay, my true task is to stand here, just beyond the realms of my own beloved forest, in a realm closer to the physical realm where Merlin and Lili currently reside.

"In this realm, I stand barefooted upon the thick snow. My toes and my feet have become tree roots, which tunnel deep into the flesh of our Mother Earth. I stand quietly, with my arms raised upward in a gesture of prayer, and from my hands and fingers, and from my head and beard, grow many limbs. At this moment, I am half tree and half man, and I do nothing but listen. I listen to the cold wind blow snow about. I listen to the stars as they sing to me, high in the heavens beyond the thick, snowy clouds. I see Lilith Moon shining bright above the snow clouds. Her song joins with that of the stars.

"Yet, while I am watching the heavens, I am noticing the life of the forest around me, the creaking and swaying of the trees in the cold, winter wind. I hear their voices whispering to me, giving me news of winter and what is happening in their realm. I feel the presence of little, furry ones, some tucked away snugly within the warmth of Mother Earth and some hunting, prowling about in the snow looking for food. Quiet, winged ones sit on my limbs waiting for the dawn. I will not be moving from this place tonight, lest I disturb their sweet slumber. Other winged ones fly through my limbs, such as the owl during her hunt for a brave, traveling mouse upon the snow.

"I think to most of you, we trees are merely unimportant things. I wonder if you think you could take the axe to us all, and you would not miss us the next day or the day after that or the day after that. But I tell you, we trees are very important, and we help keep you alive in the physical realm. We keep the stories of your ancestors within our roots and trunks and limbs and leaves. The autumn leaves that fall to the ground contain stories like old pages from a forgotten book.

"I think, for the most part, we trees love you and tolerate your ways. As we pray together, sing together, sway together in the wind, and rustle our leaves together, we hope that, at some point, you Humans will hear our songs and come to see us as part of you, for, though you are quite unaware of this fact, you Humans are walking trees. You do not take time to plant your feet into Mother Earth to gain her love and her nourishment. You do not take time, you Humans, to lift your hands to the sky as limbs and receive the love and blessing of our Creator Mother and Father and our sweet brother, Jesus. You do not stand still in the rain, and let it slake the thirst of your bodies; nor do you stand still and quiet in the silent snow, so you may learn wisdom beyond anything your great centers of learning can teach you. You are a strange grove of trees who never take the time to stand outside, so that you may receive the blessing of all Creation. No, in any type of weather, given any excuse, you flee from the healing power of the great outdoors into your dark, stuffy, boxlike rooms, where you sit in awe and worship of that square box, that false storyteller, telling you all sorts of lies. It is a sorry fact you do not know that you will find more truth from a chattering squirrel or a cawing crow than you will learn from that foolish box of light inside your home.

"I would like to pass along to you a wee idea you may think upon, and that is that you take your pale, timid selves out from your homes during some day, or better yet, some night. Plant your feet the best you can upon Mother Earth, not too far apart, but far enough to give you a strong trunk. Lift your arms to the heavens, say your prayers, and just listen. Do not think. Do not talk. Be quiet for once, and just listen. If you wish to do this with a friend or a group of friends or family, fine. You will become your own little grove of trees, as long as you all remain quiet, and do not talk. You will learn to hear one another, but it will not be through the words of your mouth. Perhaps, if you are quiet or sincere enough, a passing squirrel will have a word with you. Perhaps the trees around you, who have stood there much longer than the few moments you have, will fill your spirit with more wonders than you can even conceive of.

"I, True Tom, grow tired of speaking so much at one time. I feel my skin and my clothing becoming hard and transforming into comforting, protective bark. My hair is becoming leaves, and I grow weary. Some day you may see me, Human, a tree with leaves in the midst of a bright, white winter, a tree with green leaves when all the trees around have shed theirs and stand open and naked to the winter winds. True Tom bids you farewell and wishes you true roots in the life that you lead. May you find your way back to your own grove, to your own sacred place among the trees, wherever that may be. Farewell."

Tom fades away now, and in his place stands a great tree with leaves of green in the midst of a forest of barren trees. I hope some day that I will learn to be silent enough to hear the green song of the forest.

Mira, one of the Faerie Sprites, adds, "If we learn to stand still as trees, we can become like Tom, part Human, part tree, part Faery, part tree, a green man, or a green woman. Right out of the mist, we will step, with leaves in our hair and wildness about our eyes, kin to the animals and trees and to all Creation. To the Faerie and Humans who love Creation, we will be the Green People. True Tom is a guardian of the forest and all the animals who live within and even the occasional Human who lives there. Sometimes you can see him strolling through the forest, singing loudly and laughing, or sometimes he goes silently and turns into a tree, the better to watch over his forest unseen. Those who enter the forest with disregard for it do not see Tom watching them, and, in that way, he takes them quite by surprise when he comes upon them. Tom still watches over the forest in the realms of Tír na nÓg, and he has been known, even today, to enter the physical Human realm. Do not be surprised, especially in the mountains of Appalachia, if you hear reports from Humans of a Green Man haunting the forest and protecting the animals there."

Zoeser and Telia

Here Carol speaks of her first meeting with one of the Gnomes. "One day as I prepared to begin a spirit journey, a brown, wooden box appeared in my inner vision. Inside the box were various rocks, and I particularly noticed a beautiful, shiny, pinkish-purple bracelet perhaps half an inch thick. It was made from a rock I had never seen before, and small crystals sparkled here and there upon it. I felt I was meant to wear this spirit bracelet, and so I took it from the box and placed it upon my wrist. One of my animal spirit companions then took me to a great tree in Tír na nÓg. Encircling the tree was a wooden table made up of three sections, covered by a white cloth. Working at the table was a dark-haired Gnome. I apologized for interrupting him, and he quickly stood up to greet me.

"He was very handsome, and his dark eyes shone with a radiant light. He wore a white shirt and black pants that came below his knees, with white leggings, and his shoes pointed up a bit at the ends. He told me his name was Zoeser, and that he had made the bracelet for me from rock that came from deep within Mother Earth, and the rock was a gift from her. I wondered about the color, and he said men dig and tear with their machines, but they cannot go deep enough to find rock like this. I wondered then how the Gnomes find such rocks, and he showed me how some caves lead deep down within the Earth.

"At a Grove Gathering a short time later, I asked for more information about this journey. The Gnome I met is named Zoe, and his wife is called Telia. She has long black hair and hazel eyes. Though Zoe is his name, to call him Zoeser is like saying 'my dear friend, Zoe' instead of just saying 'Zoe.' It is a term of endearment. He told us we were old friends, and that he and his wife lived in caverns within the Earth. Zoeser agreed to speak of his work within the Earth."

"If Ban were a tunneler," began Zoeser, "he would be called Banser. It is a way to identify tunnelers like ourselves. We are not as one of your famous authors saw us; we are very friendly unless you are evil. We spend much time in the tunnels. The bracelet will help you see us and will help you journey better. The crystals in the bracelet are some of the crystal stones that lie embedded in the tunnel walls. They make the walls shimmer like twilight or sunlight through blinds. It is like a beam of sun cutting through darkness or the Holy Parents' smile upon us. We stay down there on pathways opened for us by the Holy Parents. They tell us where to tunnel. We do tend to spend a lot of time there, for that is where our homes are. The air below ground is fresh, not stale as you might think, but we still come up very often, for we enjoy the touch of the sun and the moon. You might call us troglodytes, but that is an ugly word. We refer to ourselves as womb dwellers, for we dwell within the womb of the Great Mother.

"We have great halls hollowed out by water and beautiful caverns with shining, crystal pillars. We sing, and our voices are reflected off the rocks.

Fish live in our caves, but no big white eyes stare out at us, as your author wrote of in his books. He saw many realms, including some of the dark realms where large, spindly, Human-like creatures with bulbous eyes could reach out to grab you. We do not live in those realms. We carve windows in caves with fewer crystalline rooms, and we make our bedrooms there. We place very elaborately colored crystal glass in the windows, and the crystals in the walls shine through the crystal glass. The crystal light is so nurturing that plants, trees, and waterfalls can be found there.

"The rock your bracelet is made of is called Quilitite. It is never seen upon your Earth. You cannot find it even with all your monstrous machines, which we dislike intensely, for they create large gaping holes in the flesh of the Great Mother. It is rape. When we dig, we do not cover mountains with craters, left as open sores to rot. We also dislike your trash dumps where you bury garbage in the Great Mother. She tries to transform it, but it is not a pleasant thing. We know where to dig, for we are told. Some of the caverns were opened many, many millennia ago. In areas where we are to dig, the earth is soft; yet we do not have cave-ins, and our tunnels are firm. Your monstrous machines cannot go as far as we can, for we have gone to the heart of the Great Mother and been welcomed there. It is a green place with trees and animals and grass and glittering stone and waterfalls and streams and twilight, and the moon and sun rise. It happens by will and the love of the Holy Parents and the Great Mother. It is a mystery, but one that is better untouched and unmolested by science."

CHAPTER VI

Meeting the Elves

It was not until the morning of our fourth Grove Gathering that I spied a company of Elves, mounted upon Unicorns, entering our yard. As they sat on their mounts, I was overwhelmed by a sense of how tall and stately they appeared and the aura of dignity they portrayed. Like the Gnomes, their features were strong and beautiful. They dismounted, and I saw a tall, dark-haired Elf, who wore his hair long, down to his shoulders. As he approached, I saw his dark eyes focus on us, and I considered running back into the house and shutting the door, so uneasy did I become in their presence. Beside him walked a beautiful, female Elf, with long, reddish-blonde hair and bright blue eyes. I was told by a Gnome standing close to us that the male and female Elves were King and Queen of their realm.

Close beside them walked one who appeared to be a warrior Elf, a proud, noble figure with flowing red hair pulled back into a warrior's topknot at the top of his head. His flashing, green eyes scanned the field, searching for any possible enemies who might consider doing harm to his King and Queen. Within his short, well-kept, red goatee, his white teeth flashed in a warrior's smile. Walking behind them, I noticed other Elves. One was a beautiful, tall, slim, dark-haired female Elf with smiling brown eyes. Walking close to her, their arms linked, was a red-haired female, also beautiful, with very kind green eyes. Walking near them was another male Elf with kind, dark brown eyes, who wore his long, dark hair pulled back into a ponytail, with a closely trimmed goatee.

The King and Queen stood before me, and I was not sure whether to bow or whether I should speak first. Though at first I found them intimidating, I noticed they were smiling at us, and their eyes appeared friendly and compassionate. The male introduced himself first as Arawn, High King of the Elven Realm. He introduced his High Queen, Rhiannon, who rules jointly and equally beside him. Then King Arawn introduced the general of his armies and his companion protector, Yurigel, the Stouthearted. Yurigel introduced the others to us. The beautiful, dark-haired Elf was his wife, Niamh. She, in turn, introduced the lovely, red-haired Elf as Dr. Maurena, and, finally, the dark-haired gentleman Elf was introduced as her mate or husband, Dr. Nile. The two doctors are the King and Queen's personal physicians, and they also are King and Queen of their own smaller Elven kingdom. We asked Rhiannon to speak here of how she and Arawn govern in Tír na nÓg.

Arawn and Rhiannon

"I am Rhiannon, High Queen of the Elves, and my husband is Arawn, High King of the Elves. Arawn and I have been a king and queen for a little over thirty-one hundred years, for we came into those roles as very young Elven. Our kingdom was one of those within the physical world that was driven out of that world. We chose to follow King Manannán, the Elven High King, into the next realm, and we ourselves assumed the positions of High King and Queen about two thousand years ago. Like the priestesses and priests, Gnome or Elven, we believe in the twin strands, in that we give counsel, and we take counsel. We do not rule our kingdom with an iron rod, but with a gentle touch. My husband and I rule together with all the people who live in our kingdom.

"We are now protectors of the Grail, as it passed into our hands long ago. We lead armies back to the realms closest to Earth, as King Manannán did, for we strive to protect those Humans and others of our family of Creation from the evil intent of those who have no love in their heart for the Holy Mother. We strive to serve the Holy Parents as Queen and King and fulfill their wish that the Holy Father and Holy Mother and Christ and Mary will once again be remembered by the Humans in the physical realm, and that they will protect the Great Mother Earth and cherish and nurture her as she has nurtured us.

"Besides our day-to-day task of ensuring that all our subjects' needs are met, we, with the help of the Holy Family, try to care for the kingdom as a mother cares for her child and to ensure that fairness and justice rule. We are the high priests of our kingdom. If we physically suffer, so does our kingdom physically suffer. If we spiritually suffer, so does our kingdom spiritually suffer. We are the reflection of the Holy Parents. We are the King and Queen of Tír na nÓg. We are servants of the Holy Parents and servants of our people. That is what we do, and, as Queen and King, we strive to reflect the light of the Holy Parents and the Holy Family clearly."

Niamh and Yurigel

Niamh is the Elven Lady of the Lake for Tír na nÓg, and she tells here of her life as a priestess.

"My husband, Yurigel, and I serve as advisors to Queen Rhiannon and King Arawn. We also serve our people, or the realm, as priestess and priest. My husband is known as Lord of the Land. This title is given to one who not only shows great battle prowess, but is also highly spiritually developed and humble of mind and manner. It is his duty as Lord of the Land or High Priest of the Land to protect the spirit nature and the physical nature of the Great Mother. In protecting the land, he protects the queen and king who represent the land, for while their physical and spiritual wellbeing is intact and complete, so is the land, but when they are spiritually or physically ill, the land suffers also. They are linked directly with the Great Mother. Their energy helps maintain the Great Mother Earth physically and spiritually. They contribute, with many other beings, to maintaining the wellness and health of the Great Mother, so they themselves can become taxed and require the presence of their Elven and Gnome doctors.

"King Arawn and Queen Rhiannon have held this office and undertaken this task for thousands of years. They are strong spiritually and mentally and are physically hale, and it is my husband's duty and honor to ensure that they are protected, for when they are strong, so is the Great Mother. When the Great Mother is ill, they too are ill, for they are tied that closely to the land. They dwell in the spiritual aspect or spiritual self of the Great Mother, which is very healthy for it is the original Garden. As long as they dwell in the spiritual heart of the Great Mother, they will maintain their health. Were they to leave that spiritual nature of the Great Mother and venture deeper into the Human realm, and their bodies were to become more solid and physical, in all likelihood, they would become weaker or sickness might infect them.

"It is true, due to the conditions of the physical part of the Great Mother, that they cannot become more physical, for this might cause their death, and they have what we understand from the Holy Parents to be many more thousands of years to rule this land justly. It has been predicted that one day they will be able to become more physical, walk in the sight of Humans, and not suffer any ill effects. Before that time, however, the Great Mother Earth must go through a very powerful cleansing process and rid herself of much disease in the form of cancers or tumors that threaten her very existence.

"The spiritual reflection of the land my husband protects is the realm of the great forests that surround our kingdom. The kingdom, or capital, and the smaller kingdoms dwell within great forests, and it is these forests he protects and safeguards with his very life. He is the consort, companion, and mate to the Lady of the Lake, who is I.

"My task and my blessing is to be a reflection of the Holy Mother or of the Great Mother Earth or the Goddess herself, as my husband's is to be the reflection of the Holy Father or Father Pan or God. Obviously, we are not the Holy Parents. We are not God and Goddess. We are just a reflection, and we hold this position or place of office to remind the people of the Holy Parents. I also serve to protect the waters of the lakes, streams, and rivers that flow through our realm, including the wells and underground streams. I am the comforter and nurturer of the land and of the Great Mother and her people, as my husband is the protector and the nurturer of the land and of Father Pan and his people. We are counselors of our own people and of the Fair Folk of other realms. True to our task, we give counsel and take counsel from the people.

"We also very much enjoy our home business. My husband and I act as the royal mead makers for our majesties and the realm and for others of the Fair Folk. We both enjoy this task very, very much. We also have people who work with us (not for us, but with us), who are training as apprentices or mead masters in their own right. We make mead using old Elven recipes and recipes from Gnomes and others of the Faerie. The most comforting mead, and, in my opinion, perhaps the most nurturing mead, are our Elven and Gnome brands of mead, but the most powerful mead, which a warrior might drink before going into battle, are our Centaur and our Dragon mead, made from recipes handed down to us from the Centaurs and Dragons themselves.

"We also train the young men and women in the duties of warriors. I am a warrior trained and a captain of my own company. In cases of extreme emergency, I am allowed to lead my company into battle. There have been times when I have led my company, and my husband, the General, was notified after I had already left."

"She is an excellent warrior," interjected Yurigel, "true and brave, and none may stand before her with sword and shield, but I tend to worry about her in the field. Yet I understand she must sometimes be sent, and I myself have sent her into battle."

"Oh, but my beloved," replied Niamh, "that has rarely happened in the last few thousand years."

"It has happened enough," responded Yurigel, "that each trip you have made into battle has been etched firmly into my memory."

"I am a warrior," said Niamh, "as my father before me, as my mother before me, as my sisters before me. The one who taught me my duties or tasks as a priestess and who eventually trained me to take up the role of Lady of the Lake was my sister, Ealilithea, who also was quite a formidable warrior and still is today.

"My husband and I also train novice priests and priestesses, just as my sister trained me, and my mother trained her, and on back to my great, great, great grandmother. It is a teaching that takes several years to complete and requires the novice priest or priestess, when they come of age or become recognized as an adult in their community, to leave home and journey to a small colony within the forest. This colony is known by Humans as Avalon; indeed, it is the same Blessed Isle that once existed in ancient Britain before its retreat into the mists. At Avalon, the novices are cared for and watched after by the priestesses and priests who live at the colony. My husband and I, because of our many, many duties, cannot live at Avalon, but we journey there often to lead classes, perform ceremonies, and act as counselors to the novices. With the other priests and priestesses, we help lead the novices through their final initiation or training. Though they enter the Grove as novices, upon completing their journey through the Labyrinth, they are reborn as priestesses and priests.

"Without going into great detail concerning the training, it does take, in your Human timeframe, twenty-four years to pass through the process, although, in reality, it is a lifelong process. The teachings are taken in sets of three years each. Every three years, the students are asked to complete levels of tasks, or to reach a degree of achievement and demonstrate that to the elder priests and priestesses within their house, for they are sent to live within groupings we refer to as houses. A house is not only a physical place or structure; it is seen as a family unit. The novice priestesses and priests never, ever, give up links or ties to their physical families, but they become a part of these houses, and their family ties there are very strong. They become like blood brothers and sisters.

"These houses, with their den father or den mother, offer support to the struggling novices as they strive to achieve their levels or their lessons. These houses also are support-based by the other novices or students, who encourage their fellow students. You see, no one in these different clans is left behind. One does not graduate unless the entire house graduates, so the student or novice who is not as quick as the other students of the house will be assisted by them and by the den mother and father, who will encourage, nurture, and support the struggling novice who is slower than the rest until he or she catches up. No sense of anger is felt towards the one who lags behind, nor is that person exiled from the house and the priestess and priest colonies. That is something that does not happen, and our novices are taught in a way that all will learn in their time. Never is there a shortage of priests or priestesses; nor is there an overabundance, for not everyone wishes to become priests or priestesses. Those who do usually become aware of it very young, even as children. We do not have the right to declare one unfit for the role of priestess or priest, and, therefore, we strive to help them. We usually have eight sets of three years, and the final year is spent preparing to accept the robe of priest or priestess. In special situations, because of their skills, individuals may be allowed to move ahead, but they still dwell in their house. They may actually don the robe of a priestess or priest and dwell in the house and assist the others who began with them as classmates or novices.

"We do not isolate the students and keep them away from their families during the years of their training. On our holidays and once a year, the novices or students are sent back to their homes to visit their families and keep the bond strong, but they do spend most of their time at the colonies. Yurigel and I travel to these colonies and take up our roles as Lady of the Lake and Lord of the Land, or High Priestess and Priest. In these times, Gnomes, Elves, and other of the Faerie are trained together and live in the same houses together. Therefore, you may have a house made to support not only the Elves and Gnomes, but also others, like Sprites and Centaurs and Merfolk and others of the Faerie, who are always represented there as priestesses or priests.

"Within these houses are clans, but each student or novice has his or her own room. We think that privacy and time to be alone are very important. They are quite comfortable little rooms with beds and bookshelves and places to hang personal belongings. After all, these rooms are theirs for twenty-four years, so they must allow the personality to flow. Within a house, males and females live together in separate rooms. As you probably can guess, many times novices find their soul mates there. Provided it does not interfere with their studies, they may form a tryst, in a sense, or a bonding or a promising to one another, and this is considered acceptable within the community. As they join hands or grasp each other's hand, a white cloth is wrapped about them. This shows to others that they have formed this tryst or bond between them. It is not marriage, *per se*; it is more like an engagement with a potential union later on.

"Now remember these novices or students are adults. They may be young, but they are still adults, and they will have romantic interludes. In our houses, however, we ingrain in them the responsibility to hold themselves up to be as spiritually pure as possible. They are expected to follow a code of ethics to ensure they are able to complete their studies and not cause harm or become a distraction to themselves or anyone else. It is important that, if a tryst or partnership or engagement forms, it will not be at the expense of their own studies or those of their partners or others around them. When one has these soul mate trysts, one must respect the privacy and the feelings of others, so the engagements are held discretely. Others will know of them, but romance, though allowed, will not be allowed to overwhelm anyone. To have a romance, the ones in love must be true to themselves, to their classmates, and to their studies, so that it does not become bothersome, distracting, or disrupting to their own lives or to the life of the house or the kingdom. Respectful discreteness is advised.

"Never are our students looked down upon by students of a level higher than themselves, for that is not allowed. Were a student at a higher level to look down upon someone at a lower level, not only would it would be greatly discouraged, but also that student might even be dropped down to the lower level and moved into the house of the student they had looked down upon. You can imagine, then, that students do not do that. It is an unwritten rule, one that has never needed to be enforced or used during my time.

"During the last year, the students or novices spend much time in the woods by themselves seeking their visions or destinies, or they sit and try to see all pathways that connect throughout Creation and connect with them. They try to see the past, present, and future, and what their role or destiny is in these pathways, and what options they have. After a period of living as hermits, the young men and women are brought back together so they can become used to being with others again. They renew friendships and speak of what they have experienced in their isolation, meditation, or communion in harmony with nature and of the part they wish to play in it or have been shown they should play. During the last few days, the excitement mounts as families come from all over the realms to be with their children in the great Grove at the roots of the Great Tree.

"Forming a very solemn, but beautiful, ceremonial procession, the students are led into the Grove, while their families watch from within the rings they form about the roots of the Tree. Both male and female students arrive in very simple white robes. The white denotes purity, simplicity, and pureness of spirit. They are given their vows, they repeat them, and they are then handed their staffs and their heavier robes. The students don their priest and priestess robes, and the elders place wreaths of flowers and leaves about their heads as crowns. The assembly of families and elders and others who form a ring about the roots of the Great Tree give a great shout, and the singing begins, the praising of the Holy Parents, Christ, and Mary, and this usually lasts far into the night.

"So overcome with spirit are we that we do not notice the passing of time. Musical instruments are brought out, and stories are told by the new priests and priestesses themselves as they participate in their role for the first time as confirmed, true priestesses and priests. Early in the morning, usually with the children asleep on their parents' laps, food or breakfast is served by the priests and priestesses themselves and the novices, and again more songs are sung, more music is played, and the dancing begins. By midday, others arrive with the food for the feast, and we gather at tables set up about the Great Tree. The priests and priestesses themselves are served first by the families and others of the community, so that the teaching that priestesses and priests serve and are served, that they give counsel and take counsel, is fulfilled."

Now it was Yurigel's turn to speak. "My wife and soul mate, Niamh, has already spoken on what it is like to be an elder or wise one, so let me talk more on my other task, or actually it is our other task. Young men and women come to my men and officers, including my wife, Niamh, to be trained to be warriors, to learn to defend themselves, and to defend their people and other peoples of justice. They also learn to defend the Great Mother. We not only instill confidence in them, self-assurance and a bit of bravado, but we instill in them a deepening sense of spiritual connection and concern for the welfare of all Creation. We teach them to feel concern for every blade of grass, every stone, every tree, every animal, stream, and hill, and for the people themselves, the Gnome and the Elven and the rest of the Fair Folk. We also feel concern for Humans, though we cannot be of as much help to them as we would like, for they are like a man who is drowning in deep water. When you swim out to try to save him, you are almost drowned yourself by his desperate struggles to survive. We teach them, also, to deepen their bond with the Holy Parents, with Christ and Mary, and with the saints, like Brighid and Joseph of Arimathea.

"The training of our warriors is nothing like the way Humans train their warriors or soldiers. The Human way is to beat the soldiers down, take away their manhood or their womanhood and their sense of self-assurance, and gut them of any self-identity, so they become as empty as a rag doll or curled into a tight ball afraid of being hurt. Then you attempt to resurrect these men and women as soldiers. Where is their spirit? It has been stolen and is held by the commanders and officers, like genies in bottles, to be released only in time of war or shattered on the ground in an act of sacrifice.

"It would be better to make contact with the spirit already there within the young men and women. Teach them to open the doors to that spirit, to the Holy Mother and Father, that they may feel their love, their strength, and their courage, for in this way they will become better fighters. They will hold up better under insurmountable odds, and, though they may be afraid on the battlefield or in the very act of giving their life for their country, they will do it with honor, bravery, and courage.

"It is hard for Humans to understand what I am saying, but, instead of stealing spirit, fortify it, and make it stronger. Exercise it, and make it stronger, not just the physical body, but the spirit, so that when the body gives out, with all its muscles and training, the spirit, being very muscular and strong, will have the strength to go on and nurture the soldier like a mother nurtures her child. The spirit will raise the body up from the ground, from the dust, though it be wounded or frightened or exhausted, and the soldier will stand and fight to the end if need be. There will be no surrender, no retreat, but only victory, either victory through death or the giving of one's life for one's loved ones, one's country, the Great Mother herself, and the Holy Parents, or victory in driving the enemy back and driving them from the land into surrender. At that moment, when a soldier has the enemy under control with his hands, he will show the enemy mercy instead of slaughter. The fame of the brave, conquering warriors, who showed compassion and mercy instead of inflicting slaughter, will not be seen as a sign of weakness. When the defeated enemy returns to their lands, to their homes, to their wives and children, and to their husbands, they will speak of these warrior soldiers in awed tones. Not only will these governments think twice about waging battle against such brave warriors, but perhaps that light the defeated ones brought back from the battlefield will also spread in their own spirits, fill their own Grail Cups, and spread out to the land and beyond. A country, a nation of people, a land may be healed in defeat rather than in victory.

"We do not pamper the soldiers and wipe away their tears; we do stretch their spirits and exercise them until they are fit for battle. Perhaps you are wondering how we do such things and what teachings we provide. Never fear—that is a topic for another book, another time. Perhaps you could call it *Yurigel and the Art of War*, and my name will live alongside the other famous warrior, Sun Tzu, on the bookshelves. We do train them in the art of weaponry, but we do not use weapons such as your rifles or pistols or grenades. Our weapons may seem primitive due to the standards of your army—your high-tech, your blinking lights and flashing machines, your flying crafts, and vessels that swim underwater like whales. We do not have missiles or spears that strike the earth to destroy a city and a land, and, perhaps, if enough of them are used, a world. Still, I would match our weapons against yours any day, for magic lives in our weapons—in our swords, in our spears, in our bows and arrows.

"Magic lives and breathes in our shields, in our helms, and in our armor, which can deflect any bullet your weapons may fire, any missile your armies may launch, and any explosion you may conjure up. With our mounts, the Unicorns, and their stout hoofs, we can crush your tanks and outrun your soldiers. Our swords alone can cut through any armor plates you may use for protection, and your flying machines or crafts will have very little effect against the great Dragons who fight with us. We Elves have learned many things since our last battle with Humans long ago, and one lesson we have learned is to stand united and not fight one another. Another lesson is to have a stronger link with the Holy Parents, and yet another is to practice, as we have been doing for thousands and thousands of years, observing Humans, improving our techniques, and improving our weapons.

"We have no desire (at least not the Fair Folk in my realm) to invade Human lands or wage war on them, for to do that would be contrary to the wishes of the Holy Parents. I am not just bragging about how wonderful my army is, though, as a general, I would be expected to do that, would I not? I am not saying this because I wish to fight Humans or hold a grudge against them—quite the contrary—but I am trying to make Humans understand there is more to your spiritual laws and to your reality than you understand. The spiritual laws of the Holy Parents are more powerful than any army or navy or flying force you may send against us in the field. The Holy Parents' spiritual laws of nature can withstand any nuclear blast and any weapon that mankind (and I am indicating the lack of female respect and honor that you hold in your culture by referring to your people as mankind and not womankind) could send against us and the Holy Parents.

"I am not saying the Holy Parents are only on the side of the Faerie and not of Humans. The Holy Parents are on everyone's side, and Christ and Mary are on the side of all Creation, but the Holy Parents will help the ones who try to live a just life, a life of compassion and honor for all Creation. They will tend to help those who try to live by those laws. The ones who have disrespect, no compassion, and a lack of honor—no matter how well-trained or advanced their machines are or how grand or advanced their society is—will not be able to withstand the primitives if the primitives have the Holy Parents fighting for them and holding their side of the field in battle against the enemy.

"After this long tale, or this long pathway of words we have taken together, the quick of the tale and the short of the whole matter is that we train our soldiers well. The young women and the young men are trained together, with sleeping quarters together. They respect one another, for, if they did not, they would have to deal with their commanders or officers, or what you refer to as sergeants, if there was any sexual harassment involved. However, our young people do not ever seem to have that in mind; perhaps because we are not raised so prudishly as in your Human cultures, where sex becomes so taboo or naughty that it is kept inside like a boiling teapot that must let off steam or scream. We do not have this problem, so the male and female soldiers train together, and our officers are male and female. Women are honored just as men. Some of the best fighters are women, and some of the best fighters are men.

"Training usually takes between nine and ten years, but, in reality, it lasts indefinitely during the time the warriors are in the service of the Holy Parents. We allow the soldier warriors time to go home to be with their family, for to isolate them from their families would be to have them forget who and what they are defending and laying their lives down for. Much of the Elven warrior training is very similar to that of the Gnome warriors, for often we train and then serve together on the same battlefield. Once a soldier, always a soldier. A good example of this is the Gnome, Thurisaz, who, at the ripe old age of ten thousand years, is still a formidable warrior.

"Not all of the Gnome and Elven are warriors. All of the Faerie receive some warrior training, so that they may be called upon in times of extreme battle needs, but there is a definite warrior class. Painters or musicians are not held above anyone else in the community because of their skills; for this reason, neither are warriors held above others just because they are warriors. Many of us, because our lives are so long, develop multiple skills. We may become, during our long, nearly immortal life, a soldier warrior, musician, priest, baker, or whatever we choose. Why should life be boring? You Humans have one task, one job, and then you count down the days until you can retire and sit by your cottage in a rocking chair, waiting for the dust that surrounds your bones to fall off, so that you may die and return to the spirit world. What type of life is that? Nay, I tell you it is better to enjoy every moment of life! I am speaking to you in Human terms; enjoy every breath, every touch of life upon your flesh. Enjoy the beating of your heart, the circulation of your blood, the sense of your nose and eyes, and the crazy thoughts that go through your Human mind. Enjoy that, as it is a gift from the Holy Ones.

"Though we are more spirit than physical, we of the Tuatha Dé Danaan enjoy our lives, though we know there is really no death. Whether you are Faery or Human or some other, you live forever. It just seems that the Human transition of stepping through another doorway, which you perceive as death, is more dramatic. You should fix that; make it less dramatic, for in our realm, those who leave our realm walk the wooded pathways to the Holy Parents. We know they do not die; they live on forever and ever, often thinking of us as we do of them. Many times, they come back to visit us, and they are happy in the Mother and Father's realm. They are not these ghosty things Humans are so excited about. You know, it is odd, but most of the ghosties are Humans. Oh, sometimes you may have a ghosty dog or a ghosty cat, for animals have been with Humans too long. But most of the ghosties you have are Humans—funny. My point is that they do not realize they can live forever, and so they are afraid to go on. Perhaps Humans would never have to die, their bodies never turn to dust, if they truly came to understand they are immortals like us. Maybe, though, it is better they do not realize this, for there would be too many Humans here on the Great Mother, and no one would ever have a chance to live.

"Speaking of death and being a soldier is to know that you may some-times have to sacrifice your life. There is ever a risk that a Gnome or Elven or other soldier of the Fair Folk might have to give their life in battle. When this happens, we always recover the body, and, even if for some reason we could not, the Holy Parents would come and recover it themselves. Always, though, we have recovered the body, and our loved ones we take as far as we can on the wooded pathways, and we leave them in a meadow with a stone beneath their head. We lay their sword beside them and wrap them in their cloak to keep them warm and kiss them on the head. We tell them to hurry and take the path to the Holy Parents and then to hurry back to us. Sometimes our departed loved ones remain within the comforting love of the Holy Parents, but sometimes they heed the call of their families in Tír na nÓg who miss them, and they return to us as children. They may say, hello, remember me, I was your son, I was your daughter, and I am back.

"It has happened, too, when a soldier, male or female, with a great wound passes, after only a few days, they will walk back into our commu-nity as hale and hearty as ever, yet with a slight forgetfulness. Even those who are born again knowing who they were before do not remember all the secrets that transpired in the realm of Holy Parents. When they remember those things, it is time to move on. Only the traveling teachers remember those secrets, but they cannot stay with us forever. They may stay for a hundred years, but then they have to travel on.

"Our soldiers have no real fear of death. It is the Hobgoblins and Trolls and Ogres who have a fear of death. When they die, their spirits usually stay within their bodies until they become wise enough to realize they can leave them. They may sometimes live for quite some time in their decaying husks, bemoaning their fate, but eventually I think they all realize they can leave their wretched shells. If they are foolish enough, they may come back into such bodies or perhaps move on.

"How can I tie up the loose ends here? All right, let me try. We exercise and build muscle on our warriors, both male and female equally, both spiritually and physically. We teach them to use their weapons well—weapons that are filled with magic, that breathe magic, and that can with-stand weapons of your realm easily. We train our soldiers to have love for the Holy Parents and all Creation. We hope the Holy Parents will see our sincerity and that we rule the battlefield with compassion and mercy, so, if it is their will, they will be on our side. Our soldiers have no fear of death for they know we are all immortal, that our vessels can be destroyed or damaged, that our bodies can be mended, or, from the old damaged vessels, a new Grail can be formed. Sometimes we must take our vessels, our bodies, our Grails, directly to the Holy Parents that they, by their very hands, can mend them themselves, and welcome us back home.

"Not only do we train in weapons and the use of weapons, and fitness of the body and spirit through long marches and camping within nature (which for us of the Fair Folk is not a chore), but we also have intensive training sessions in the use of musical instruments. Believe it or not, sounds sometimes help to win the war before the battle begins. There have been times when chanting or war cry trilling has driven the enemy from the fields. Our soldiers learn to use their voices like a weapon. Instead of using the musical quality of the voice to produce sweet sounds that cause the birds to sing, the soldiers can use notes entwined in Celtic knots. As they attempt to follow the pattern of the music, these sounds confuse and dismay the enemy, striking their very spirits like lashes of a whip and driving them howling from the battlefield.

"Likewise, chanting stories or sayings of old can sometimes take the spirit out of the enemy and cause them to wonder why they are fighting a war in the first place. I believe Humans refer to this as propaganda. With the right propaganda, they wonder why they are on the field and not at home in their caves or burrows or under their rocks. Likewise, the gentle sound of stringed instruments or pipes or drums can ease their spirits, touch their hearts, and drive the evil out of them. It can drive the dirty spots out of their spirit, so that they realize it is against the Holy Parents' wishes to fight us. They find they are not so far away from the Holy Parents as they think, and they can come back home, and so they quit the field this way.

"You see, the learning of musical instruments may be, as your culture says, an artistic thing to do. Yet it also exercises the spirit and the body and strengthens the warriors themselves. For example, does not your modern army use sounds, as when they set up their speakers or their horns outside an enemy encampment when they are laying siege to them? They will play music that often is not very pleasing to the enemy all day and all night, so the enemy has no sleep and loses their will to fight. We also use this tactic. Sometimes it is not possible or humane to destroy their water or their food supply, but we can take away their ability to sleep or get rest. Then they begin to make mistakes and lose discipline, and their armies begin to fall apart. They lose the will to fight or, even better, become so exhausted that they fall asleep during the battle.

"We try at first to avoid any war or skirmish and strive instead to settle disagreements by diplomatic means. Should diplomacy fail, we try to end the battle before it begins by techniques such as these, so that the enemy may well lose the urge to fight, and it may become a peaceful battle, instead of one filled with broken bones, horrible wounds, and death. Then, if these techniques do not work, and the enemy is more stouthearted, stubborn, or just plain foolish, we use physical means. The three strands of military law, therefore, are diplomacy and negotiation, peaceful means of dissolution (dissolving the battle before it begins), and, if all else fails, armed conflict."

Maurena and Nile

Maurena, Elven queen and healer, begins the story of how she and her husband came to dwell in Arawn and Rhiannon's realm.

"This is the story of how my husband, Nile, was king of a realm next to the physical Earth realm and how his kingdom was overrun and destroyed. Nile and I, in fact, had a friendship with some of the Humans who lived in that realm, for they were not like most of the warring Humans who caused such grievous wounds on our people. Understandably, however, my husband's father was angry at the loss of many lives in his kingdom and the encroachment of many Humans, as they expanded their physical realm and laid claim to the spiritual realm and our kingdom. At that time, Humans had power, for we did not know how to stop them. They knew how to actually enter the spirit realm connected to the physical realm and expand their territory, so that an area once under the control of the Fair Folk thus came under control of the Human folk.

"This does not happen anymore. The Holy Parents have put an end to that ability in Humans; nor do the Fair Folk have permission to lay claim to the physical realm, at least not at this time. We are able now to defend our realms more efficiently, for we have thousands of years of practice and training and experience. There has also been a spirit and physical transformation that now bars the way between Humans and our realms. As the realms travel farther and farther away from the Earth or the physical realm, the beings who travel these forest pathways must be pure in spirit. Otherwise, they will not be able to progress much farther without being absorbed into the light, entering the tunnel, or, as you Humans see it, experiencing death. Because Nile and I and others of our court at that time refused to sever our friendship and make war on the Humans who treated us so well and fought at our side against our Human enemies, my dear husband's father disowned him."

Nile continued the story, but it was clear to us, even after the passing of hundreds of years, that it was still not easy for him to speak of these events.

"It was a painful experience being an outcast from my father. The survivors of our intermediate family were my father, my sister, her daughter (my niece), and I. My mother and my other brothers had perished in earlier battles with Humans. They had died either as warriors or were caught unaware and became victims in battle. This had hardened my father's heart against the Humans, for his heart was broken from their loss. My heart was broken, also, but I refused to sever the relationship with the Human community, for, in all the battles where my family was killed or where I lost a family member, our Human allies or friends fought by our side. Sometimes they gave their very lives to try to protect us, but still my father could not look upon a Human face and not feel hate, rage, and grief. Our Human friends had died alongside us, and we shed our blood together as we fought the waves of the Human hordes who attacked our kingdoms. I, myself, while wounded and bleeding, had dragged my Human comrades into the cool quietness of the forest, for there was no one left to help me. With my own hands, I had buried them in the quiet wood away from the field of battle. I could not betray them.

"My father, in a fit of rage, disowned me and sent us from our kingdom. Some, of course, went with me, including Maurena, my wife, and my younger sister and her little daughter, and others of our Elven friends. All totaled the people who left with me would be just over one hundred. We did not leave my father's kingdom completely, but dwelt in the realms just beyond it. Many times, we entered the kingdom to fight alongside my father's armies and harass the Human armies. We would swoop in on our mounts, sometimes before the arrival of my father's armies, and strike and harry the Human flanks. In those days, the ancient Humans were not as well organized, and they marched or charged haphazardly, every man for himself. Many times, we would strike blows to distract them, as my father's armies crashed down upon them. Still, there were too many of them, and my father's armies began to weaken.

"It was especially painful after the battles, whether we had carried the day or not, to be chased out of the realm by my father's soldiers and threatened bodily, though we had fought alongside them and some of us had died that day. After a time, though we lost soldiers, our ranks began to swell, for other Elven in the kingdom saw (and it hurts my heart to say this) the injustice done by my father, and we were slowly transformed from a small rebel band into a small army. Each day, we would ride in on our mounts, sometimes before my father's armies, sometimes alongside them, but at a distance, so we would not fight a battle amongst ourselves. Then we would disengage from the enemy if we did not carry the day and ride out and try to leave the scene of the battle before my father's Elven armies would turn against us and fight us, for we did not wish to shed any Elven blood. Within my ranks from the very beginning, within the hundred soldiers, there were Humans. I would say perhaps twenty-three Humans rode with us, and, again, as our armies swelled in ranks, other Humans dwelt with us as family. Some of them still survive today and dwell with us still. These are the Humans you find scattered about the realm where we now live.

"During a great battle, when we fought to keep our last hold or grip upon our kingdom in the realm closest to the Earth, as a man hangs from the side of a cliff by his fingernails, we met in battle the invading Humans. Unfortunately, as had become usual, we lost the battle, and many brave Elven and many brave Humans died that day on both sides. My father was wounded severely and lay dying, and some of his men came to me and asked me to go to him. He told me he was sorry for what he had done, and he loved me and wished me not to carry on the battle, but instead to lead the people of our kingdom further into the realms beyond and closer to the Holy Parents. He had heard of a mighty king and queen there named Arawn and Rhiannon, who held the realm closest to the Holy Parents and were doing great works and deeds of valor. He died in my arms, and he passed the crown to me. The crown for my mother was also brought out and given to Maurena. I followed my father's wishes and sought out Arawn and Rhiannon, and, to this day, Maurena and I are devoted king and queen under them. They are the High King and Queen, but we still maintain our titles and rule our people independently, though our kingdom is smaller than Arawn and Rhiannon's kingdom.

"When my father died in my arms, I saw many wounded about me, even Humans on the other side, and there were so few healers about. When we came to Arawn and Rhiannon, gave our allegiance to them, and pledged to be devoted queen and king to them, they embraced us as family and officially adopted us. When those of the Faerie adopt you, you are, in the eyes of all Faerie, as close as a blood brother and sister. Arawn made me and Maurena his brother and sister, as did Rhiannon.

"At this time, during the feast of acceptance, a twin fold feast to cele-brate our coming to the kingdom as devoted king and queen in our own right and also to celebrate our adoption into Arawn and Rhiannon's family, I confessed to my new brother and sister how helpless I felt on the field of battle. They spoke of how they themselves had begun training with the Gnome healers. Of course, we had Elven healers before, but the Gnome healers had many skills undreamt of by us and knowledge we sorely needed, so Maurena and I trained with the Gnome healers and became healers ourselves. To this day, many of the Faerie are trained by the Gnomes. We do have Elven and Centaur professor-healers, but Gnome professor-healers are more plentiful. It is not because they control the schools of healing; it is more because we recognize the Gnomes' gifts as masters of healing, for is it not the Green Caps who work closely with the plants here in the physical? Was it not the Gnomes who came to the battlefields and showed great courage and compassion when they performed their healings? That is why we became healers and learned to minister to the sick and wounded."

"Nile and I," Maurena continued, "do spend our time caring for our kingdom or caring for our garden. In other words, our kingdom is our garden. Time means nothing to us, so we spend much time seeing to the day-to-day affairs of our people. Our kingdom, of course, is not the size of Arawn and Rhiannon's kingdom. At this time, we have perhaps ten thou-sand people, and each has their home spread out. While Arawn and Rhian-non's kingdom is built into a great mountain, ours is built more after the manner of the Gnomes. The Red Caps' homes are usually round in shape, while the Green Caps' are also rounded, but have side rooms that take on the shape of tree roots. Our homes or burrows (and we do refer to them as burrows—it is not just a Gnome saying) are vast. They are usually circular in form, with an inner ring or courtyard in the center where our gardens can be found."

Here we asked Nile and Maurena to describe themselves. "Maurena," began Nile, "has long, red, flowing hair like waves of fire to keep one warm on a dark, cold, wintry night. Her eyes are the green of the sea, and her skin is pale like moonlight upon the snow. Her form is that of a water nymph, and she captures my heart's soul with her beauty."

"Nile is very tall," said Maurena, "and his long, black hair is the color of a raven's wing. His dark eyes are like two gray, shining stones in a clear stream, and his skin is pale like the face of the Great Mother Moon and smooth as the cheek of a fawn. His well-groomed, short goatee made of fine black hairs glistens with the gleam of a raven's breast in the sunlight. All in all, he is a beautiful man without blemish who makes my heart beat with delight whenever I see him. He is a walking song, and, wherever he walks, flowers spring up behind him and singing birds follow in his wake and go before him, announcing that he is coming."

CHAPTER VII

The Unicorn Ride

Niamh and Yurigel tell this story about their very first Unicorn ride and its unexpected consequences.

"Lili was grown-up," began Niamh, "and I was a wee bairn, and I was the last of King Manannán and Queen Áine's children. Lili was having romances and going on quests and fighting Humans, while I was still in my swaddling clothes. Sometimes she would come back home from her adventures and bounce me on her knee and put flowers in our hair, but she was to marry Merlin and travel to his realm, and I was often left alone, for she was in love.

"There was one particular young, red-haired Elf who would always get into trouble. He would run between the legs of men and try to trip them. He would sometimes pretend he was a hound and go about barking. He would run under women's dresses and pretend he was hiding as a dog. Sometimes he would sneak up on a poor, unsuspecting person, and he would worry their cloak in his teeth, giving great tugs and growling menacingly, until the poor victim would cry out for help, at which point it would take several men to pull him off."

"One of my guardian animals," Yurigel remarked, "is a hound."

"He would demand to be fed from the table," Niamh continued. "Then I thought he was having so much fun that I should become a hound, too, so there I was on my hands and knees romping through the house like a playful, young puppy. My father did not think it was so funny. Yurigel and I would play together, scuffling beneath the tables at the feasts with many barks and yips, occasionally oversetting wine flagons on unsuspecting guests. As we played together at being hounds, we grew closer, and, after that, we did many things together.

"Yurigel and I would go out into the woods and play with the Unicorns. Yurigel would call the Unicorns, and these beautiful steeds would come to us. The Unicorns were very frisky, and they told us we were much too young to ride on their broad backs, for, at that time, we were only about the size of a four or five year old Human child. One day, my beloved Yurigel very determinedly climbed on a Unicorn's back and would not get off. He demanded that the Unicorns let us ride them and carry us back to Lili and Merlin's royal wedding feast, which was taking place that very day. I cried pitifully, and one of the gentle-hearted Unicorns helped me to climb on her back, also."

Yurigel continued with the story. "The male Unicorn on whose broad back I sat turned to his beloved on whose back Niamh sat and inquired, 'My lovely one, do you recall being summoned to King Manannán and Queen Áine's wedding feast for their daughter?'

"'Why no, my dear,' she responded. 'It appears that such an invitation has somehow slipped from their royal majesties' memories.'

"I began to feel a sense of unease as the Lord Unicorn stood there, quietly reflecting on the matter. 'Perhaps, my beloved one and my people,' he called out to the others around him, 'we should journey to King Manannán and Queen Áine's royal wedding feast for their daughter and her new husband, for not to journey and present ourselves before them would bring shame upon us. Let us celebrate with them this lovely day.'"

Continued Niamh, "He said then to Yurigel, 'All right, my brave little Elven lad, I will honor your request. We will make haste with great speed to the royal court of King Manannán and Queen Áine. Away with us all.'

"The Unicorns are a proud people, and they have their own minds and hold their personal honor in high regard. The Lord and Lady Unicorn had decided to teach King Manannán a lesson, so, like the wind, away they charged toward Father and Mother's court, leading behind them a whole herd of Unicorns. I could hear their thundering hooves in our wake, like the rumbling of thunder in a severe and frightening storm. The wind rushed about me, tugging at my hair and clothing, and my small hands clutched my Unicorn's thick mane as I held on for dear life. I buried my frightened face into the back of her neck and tried to cover my head with the long flowing hair of her mane. Yurigel, though I did not see him for I was too frightened to look, gave great whoops of joy, and I could hear him singing some silly song as we neared Father's court."

Yurigel put in, "I think it was something as simple as, 'I am Yurigel, the mighty, the lord of the Unicorns.'"

"It was not so well thought out, dear," replied Niamh. "I think it was something like, 'I am riding a Unicorn. I am riding a Unicorn.' Then he would say, 'I am Yurigel, and I am riding a Unicorn.' Then he would impishly add, 'Niamh is riding one, too, and she had better hang on, or she will fall off.'

"With my beloved Yurigel's joyful song flung into the wind like startled wild geese, I could tell we had entered through the gates of my parents' court, for I could hear the surprised exclamations of the guards as they leapt out of the way of our charging Unicorns. I could not see them, for remember I was busy hiding my face in my Unicorn's mane, but I knew what the guards would be doing, for they were well trained. They did not wish to hurt us, for they had recognized our small shapes on the backs of the Unicorns; nor did our people fear the Unicorns, but instead saw them as allies or friends. Bewildered as to what they should do next, they frantically signaled to the other sentries who stood guard near the gates of the walls of my parents' inner court. As we approached my parents' inner courtyard, I lifted my head to peek around the powerful head and horn of my Unicorn just in time to see the doors of the great royal hall flung open, carried by a magic wind sent by our lead Unicorns.

"I have been told by others there that day in the royal hall of my mother and father that at first they heard a great rumbling sound. The royal guests of my parents wondered if it was perhaps the beginning of an earthquake, for the tables and plates and cups and silverware rattled and trembled on the tabletops. Then, as the sound grew louder and louder, the doors were flung open, and my parents' guests swore that the ocean herself had sent a massive tidal wave to drown them all. It was with complete surprise that they watched our first two Unicorns enter the great royal hall. Being Fair Folk and fleet of foot, my parents' royal guests and the ambassadors and dignitaries and others who had come to enjoy the royal wedding feast flung themselves to safety as the stampeding Unicorn party flowed onward like an unstoppable wave, tossing tables and chairs about or crushing them beneath their heavy hooves. I heard a strange melody—a cascading chorus of a mixture of shouts of surprise and terror and joy at such a strange amazing occurrence and shouts of anger that flowed about us as we tumbled our way through the hall.

"Suddenly, everything was quite still, and I looked straight up and saw my father and my mother standing on the royal dais. Yurigel's Unicorn spoke directly to my parents, remarking that they surely had not forgotten to invite the Unicorns to the royal wedding. Seemingly as an afterthought, he added, with a slight cocking of his head, 'Oh, and as you can see, we brought your children along with us.'

"I looked hopefully for some sign of mercy behind the grim wall of my father's expression. With his powerful voice, he replied, 'I welcome the Lord and Lady of the Unicorns and their people, and it pleases us to have their presence in our royal hall. We are quite grateful they have found our lost children and returned them to us. With your permission, I will have their nursemaids gently remove them from your backs and escort them to their chambers upstairs, where we may speak with them later concerning this event.'

"The Lord Unicorn, looking full into my father's face, in a very gentle voice, answered, 'My dear King Manannán and Queen Áine, please do not be harsh with these children, for it was they who informed us of your daughter and her husband's wedding feast, that we might come and do them honor. I must confess, and I am quite embarrassed to bring this up, but it seems our wedding invitation was misdelivered.'

"My father, though profoundly embarrassed at not inviting the Unicorns, managed to keep his face impassive. He responded, 'My Lord and my Lady, the fault of your missing wedding invitation lies with me and not with my dear wife, Queen Áine. I humbly pray your pardon for this oversight, for the Unicorns have always been strong allies of the Elven and other Fair Folk. I ask in all humbleness that you forgive my unpardonable error in not ensuring that one of my courtiers delivered your wedding invitation in a timely manner.' My father then added, 'If there is something I can do to make amends for this grave mistake, please tell me, and I will do it.'

"The Lord of the Unicorns, in his very gentle voice, replied, 'My dear majesties, since it was your lovely children who took the time to come to us and remind us of this blessed day, we ask that you lift not thy hand against them, nor punish them in any way. If anyone is to blame for the ruin to your royal majesties' hall, it is I, for in my joy and supreme happiness at the wedding between your lovely daughter, Ealilithea, and Prince Emrys, I was overcome with pleasure and wild abandonment. In our bliss, my lovely Lady and I forgot all the protocols for entering your royal hall in a stately procession, but instead rushed into your hall with the force of a hurricane. If there is to be any blame for what happened here today, lay it upon my shoulders, but spare these two darlings, for they are the light of our eyes and the fire of our hearts, and it would cause us such troubling grief to know we were the cause of their punishment. This, I humbly ask, my dear majesties.'

"My mother, Queen Áine, had witnessed this entire event with calm and graceful dignity. Since it had appeared through these proceedings that we would find no mercy from my father, I looked to my mother, and, much to her credit, her face was one of serenity and held what at least appeared to be secret amusement."

"I agree with my lovely Niamh," said Yurigel, "for I could tell King Manannán was terribly angry, and I knew that, as things stood with him, Niamh and I were doomed. Yet when I turned my frightened gaze on Queen Áine, I hoped from her gentle look that she would become our angel of salvation."

"My beautiful mother moved and stood before my father," continued Niamh, "and she said, 'My Lord and Lady Unicorn, how can I deny such a gentle request coming from such a noble people as thee. Of course, we will grant your request, and no punishment shall be laid upon these dear children, but instead they shall be embraced and covered in kisses and given cakes to eat and fine cider and mead to drink, and they will sit beside me, that I may remind them of their brave deed today.'

"I heard my father gasp, and I saw a look of complete shock cross his features. For a moment, just for a moment, my handsome, proud father looked quite comical with the look of confusion resting upon his face. But, like an unwanted guest, that look vanished, and my father smiled, at first ever so faintly, and then his smile became a very wee chuckle, which grew into a virtual storm of laughter. Then the entire court in that hall broke into laughter at what had taken place there that day.

"I felt a sense of relief, and I knew when I risked a look at Yurigel that he, too, was giddy with relief. I looked over at my dear sister, Lili, and at Merlin. Merlin, smiling at us with love and affection, shook his head in disbelief. Yet my beautiful sister, Lili, the proud treasure of my heart, was not laughing, but instead was stamping her feet in a sort of angry dance. I knew then, and I did warn Yurigel, my beloved, that it was in our best interests to stay far from her, at least for that night, which we made sure to do. For the rest of that evening, we sat close to my mother, Yurigel and I, and we were fed all sorts of sweet cakes and sweet, sparkling cider and tasty mead until our eyes grew heavy with contentment from our full bellies. We drifted off to sleep and were eventually carried up to our chambers, that we might dream the night away. I dreamt of riding on the back of a Unicorn, and I was not afraid. I might even have sung Yurigel's song, 'I am riding a Unicorn. I am riding a Unicorn, and I am not afraid.'

"My mother and my father, true to their word, never laid punishment upon us and ever afterwards spoke of this time with prideful amusement. I think it was at this time that I heard my father say, 'That young Elven lad, Yurigel, some day will be a great leader among the Elves and a great warrior. I just know it.' When I heard him say that, I was filled with such pride, for I knew that some day he would be my beloved husband.

"Merlin, being Merlin, would always laugh when he told the tale of our great adventure riding the Unicorns, and he would ruffle our hair and tell us how brave we were. My dear sister, my lovely, dear, cherished sister, Lili, forgave me the very next morning, but she warned me that on my marriage day I should not be surprised if Unicorns were suddenly to come to my wedding feast. And she, like my dear Mother and Father, kept her word."

The Wooing of Niamh

This is the twisting, turning tale of how Niamh and Yurigel came to be sacred mates.

"As we grew," Niamh began, "Yurigel and I did everything together. We were inseparable, and it was a foregone conclusion that, when we grew up, he and I would become sacred mates. When we were around what would be considered seventeen years of age in Human years, we began to awaken sexually; in other words, we began to see each other in a wholly different way. My beautiful Yurigel, being a splendid specimen of an Elf-man, would pause near (and I caught him several times) a pool of water or a still lake which reflected like a mirror. There he would admire himself, and he would flex his muscles, tousle his hair, smooth his eyebrows, and scowl and grimace, practicing his warrior face. Sometimes he would pretend he was talking to someone, perhaps a lady of the court or some royalty or nobility, using his high flowery speech, and then he would laugh and chortle in an ever so becoming manner at some joke his invisible friend was telling him. I came upon him one day when he was practicing this fine way of speech, and he became quite embarrassed and angry and told me, 'You should never sneak up behind a warrior like that, because it may be to your detriment.'

"This made me a wee bit angry, so I said to him, 'How could you even know of my approach when you were so captivated by your reflection in the pond?'"

"My reply," said Yurigel, "was that 'I was merely practicing the art of diplomacy and how to present myself in a pleasing and agreeable manner to visiting royalty that I may not shame myself before our royal guests, unlike someone I know who would waddle in like a goose and make honking sounds and embarrass herself.'"

"I became quite affronted at his remark," Niamh continued, "for I was sensitive about the slightly peculiar walk I had somehow developed as a young girl. I had, by that time in my life, managed to put it behind me, learning to walk in a graceful and ladylike, yet beguiling, manner befitting the Lady of the Lake I hoped someday to become. Now we found ourselves engaged in a swordfight of words, and I parried his insult by saying, 'I do not know why you choose to look at yourself constantly in every reflective thing you come upon. Your appearance is still that of a small boy, while in looks you are quite average, not ugly, but just average, and certainly no where near as beautiful as you think you are.'

"We were fighting a hard fought battle, but our tempers and, in fact, our blades had become sharpened by our newly emerging passion for one another."

"We had begun to look at each other in a new way," commented Yurigel, "not just as playmates, but in a sexual, hormonal way. I was actually madly in love with her."

"As I was with him," responded Niamh.

"Though everyone around us could see it," Yurigel continued, "we tried to hide it from one another. You must understand, for all of our young life, we had played together as playmates, and we had seen each other only as Yurigel or Niamh, my friend or comrade. When we were young children, we even bathed together."

"Yurigel," continued Niamh, "noticed that his ever-so-handsome reflection was tainted with embarrassment from the well-placed thrust of my insult. He replied, 'Not only are you nothing but a stick of a girl and quite plain indeed, but it appears you are also blind. If you cannot see the beautiful sun god standing before you, then there is no hope for you.'"

"At that time," said Yurigel, "being a young man, I was gloriously vain, to the point it made me foolish, for this young woman before me was, in fact, not a stick of a girl. She had the face and figure of a goddess, more lovely than the most sensual Water Nymph or Sprite or any Fair Folk or fair face who had ever walked in Tír na nÓg or any other realm."

"When he said that," Niamh continued, "and since he was standing near the pool looking into it, I kicked him with my boot. He fell into the pond face first, and I said, 'Perhaps you should go soak your head in pond mud, and, while you are at it, you should wash out your eyes that you may see more clearly. Perhaps the mud will wash out the filthy, degrading insults that have poured out of your mouth like a stream of muck from a Human privy.'

"For the first time in our lives, the two who were inseparable became separated, and we did not talk to each other for days. Of course, we would watch each other out of the corner of our eyes. Before all the other ladies of the court, whether Gnome, Elf, or other Fair Folk, if they were female, you would always find Yurigel laughing gaily, flashing his beautiful smile, and tossing his locks. He would flutter his eyelashes at any female who passed his way, and, with a merry twinkle in his bright green eyes, he would tell of his battle skirmishes and how powerful he was on the battlefield. He had been out a time or two, but he would enhance the stories."

"There was no enhancement," said Yurigel.

"Are you sure you would vanquish an entire army of Ogres yourself with no one else upon the field?" Niamh asked.

"Of course I did," Yurigel replied. "I might have had some help, but I do not remember it. That was a long time ago."

"As he was describing his battle prowess," continued Niamh, "he would flex his muscles and demonstrate the various exercises warriors would do, in order to emphasize how supple he was and how strong his arms and how powerfully built were his thighs. He would wiggle his bottom at them to show how hard it had become from many hours on horseback on the battlefield."

"It is always good," remarked Yurigel, "to be able to laugh at how foolish you were when you were young."

"Watching him do this," Niamh remembered, "I would pretend it did not bother me that he was such a silly oaf. I would say to those around me, 'Oh, there he is again, that big silly oaf. How silly he looks, and how foolish he is, being just a mere boy.' The others who were observing Yurigel's exercises of suppleness and listening to my comments would smile to themselves and try to maintain a balance of peace between us. They would keep their thoughts to themselves; yet, though I chose not to look, I would sometimes see a smile on their face or a twinkle in their eye. Perhaps they were admiring Yurigel, but they knew what was going on between us.

"I would guess that, during this time, my beloved Yurigel and I amused many people with our passionate battle of love. The older women would smile at him, and perhaps they were impressed with his suppleness and battle prowess, so they nodded their heads at him and patronized him. The young women who were unattached would ooh and aah around him and feel the muscles of his arms or pinch his taut thighs and comment on how powerful they were. They would remark on how brave he must have been on the battlefield and how handsome he was. I, being driven into a jealous frenzy, began to surround myself with hopeful paramours. I wore the most beautiful dresses I could find, both to accentuate my womanly features and also in an attempt to drive my Elven admirers wild with desire."

"She dressed provocatively," Yurigel interjected, "in low-cut gowns with surprise openings, perhaps slits, that would show off a comely leg if she positioned herself in a particular manner."

"I would stand about in my stunning gowns," said Niamh, "combing back my long, beautiful, dark hair and exhibiting its silkiness and how it glimmered in the sunlight or the moonlight. My male admirers would flatter me, and I would coo or titter at anything they said, whether it was funny or not. I would tell them how strong and handsome and clever they were, but I told them I would not choose just anyone for my sacred mate. It would have to be the one who could outrun the fastest Unicorn, who could hurl Lugh's mighty javelin the farthest, and who was able to leap higher than the mighty Salmon of Wisdom after the acorn of knowledge. Only the one who was the best at all these things could be my sacred mate, and, in my heart, I secretly hoped that my beloved Yurigel would hear these requirements to win my heart and himself take up the challenge. The sea of hopeful lovers who surrounded me all vowed to take up the quest to win my heart, and, of course, Yurigel, the Mighty, the one who had ridden upon the back of a Unicorn when he was only five in Human years, also heard of my challenge. To my delight, he took up my quest."

"At first," remarked Yurigel, "I planned to take up the challenge mainly to show that I was the best. I was not interested in winning the quest, but, if I did, I thought I would just have her as my servant girl."

"See how foolish he was?" inquired Niamh. "He thought he would own me."

"I am very fortunate the Holy Parents sowed some wisdom into my youthful mind," Yurigel commented.

"On the chosen day," continued Niamh, "I appeared, looking as stunningly beautiful as is permitted in the presence of all Creation. On that day, I tried to be more beautiful than was anything else in Creation, in my own simple female vanity and with the desperate desire that my beauty would so inflame Yurigel that he would outdo all of my other suitors. I was a little afraid, you see, that he might not be as gifted as he thought himself, for, though I knew he was gifted, I was afraid there might be someone there who was slightly more gifted. I had finally come to the realization we were both being silly, and I feared the Holy Parents might teach us a lesson. I thought unhappily about how terrible it would be to have someone else win the contest for my heart. On that fateful day, I looked out upon my suitors and all the others who had gathered to see my contest (for no Fair Folk in their right minds would even consider such a contest). I did not see Yurigel's face, and I felt a moment of sheer panic. I thought, 'He is not going to even come. I am not even worth it to him to compete in this contest, and he has chosen some other Elven to be his sacred mate.'

"It was then we heard a thundering of hooves emerging behind us, and, soon, out of the woods appeared Yurigel, riding on the back of the King of the Unicorns. His bright red hair was tied up into a warrior's topknot. His family crest of two eagles was upon the face of his shield, and his sword, which he had named Starsinger, was held high above his head. He rode out, and the crowd parted and made way for him. I could see the crestfallen looks on my other suitors' faces as they realized their stretching and flexing was no where near as impressive as my beloved Yurigel's entrance.

"Yurigel, as he dismounted from the back of the Unicorn, remarked to his fellow contestants, 'I hope you have not tired yourselves out from all your stretching and flexing, for I am not tired, and no one will be able to defeat me this day.' Then he turned and looked at me, and I saw by the expression on his face that an insult was just under the surface. Then I think he saw the tears of pure relief in my eyes that he had appeared, and I saw that other look vanish from his face like melting snow in the sunlight, sliding off a steep roof. It just vanished, and he stood quietly looking into my eyes. I saw Yurigel, my playmate, my friend, but I also saw something else—that he loved me very much.

"Then he said, 'No one will defeat me, and I will win the fair hand of the beautiful Niamh.'

"There was some grumbling from my suitors and some uneasy stamping of feet, as they realized they were perhaps doomed this day (or at least we hoped so). The Sprites had woven a special scarf for me to use for the contest. This scarf was transparent, except for the golden sparkles within it that caught the light when it was held up to the sun. I said, 'Let the contest begin when I release this scarf and end when the scarf falls to the earth. If all three tasks have not been completed by the time the scarf falls to earth, or if no one has finished, then no one will win my heart.' The scarf lifted up into the air and took straight off as if it were a bird. Luckily, such scarves are very light and magical, and I was assured by the Sprite who brought me the scarf that it would not fall until the contest was finished.

"The first event of the contest was that whoever would be my love must run faster than the fastest Unicorn, who happened to be the King of the Unicorns who had brought Yurigel to the field that day. From the clearing, the Queen of the Unicorns appeared, and she gave the King her blessing and told him to run faster than the wind. I was afraid that no one could run faster than the Unicorn. The contestants lined up next to the Unicorn King, and all waited tensely for the sound of the mighty war horn, which was usually used to begin battles, but was here used for my contest. With a mighty blast, all took off running. They were to run through a path in the forest that had many roots to trip the runners, many stones to go around, and many tree branches to reach out to entrap them. Soon the runners and my beloved Yurigel and the Unicorn King disappeared from sight, and all we could do was wait."

Yurigel took up the story here. "The pathway, as promised, was not a smooth one. It was narrow, with low branches to entangle my hair and roots and rocks to trip me. I was leaping over roots, ducking beneath branches, and leaping around trees that suddenly appeared, and I was trying to keep abreast of the Unicorn King. One fellow who had been ahead of me got his hair caught in a tree branch. Not only was I dodging tree roots and branches, I was also dodging my fellow contestants. After a time, I knew there was no one ahead of me, and, though I was a few feet behind the Unicorn, there was no one behind me, although I did hear the occasional muffled curse. I later heard one poor fellow ran directly into a tree, so that his arms and legs straddled it until he fell back into unconsciousness. What a blow it must have been to him when he awoke from a pleasant dream to find that the lover he grasped so closely was in fact a tree and not my beloved Niamh.

"We finally broke free from the forest byway and into the meadow where the Fair Folk and Niamh were awaiting me. Unfortunately, the Unicorn was far ahead of me, and my lungs felt as though they would explode, and my heart felt it would explode from grief if I did not win my beloved in this contest. Then, just before he was to cross the finish line, the Unicorn's mate ran up to him with a playful neigh and canter of her legs, and he immediately changed course. Snorting like a lustful stallion, he took off after her, and I crossed the finish line. The judges decided that I was the winner since the King of the Unicorns did not finish the race. The Queen of the Unicorns knew the King could outrun me any day, so she used her feminine wiles to arouse him and keep him from finishing the race, for how could he resist her? Yet it was also an act of mercy on her part."

"My beloved Yurigel," said Niamh, "passed the first test by the mercy of the Holy Parents and Christ and Mary, but also by the mercy of the King and the loving compassionate heart of the Queen of the Unicorns, for the Queen of the Unicorns, being a woman, knew my heart longed for Yurigel to win. She, being an authority on the art and knowledge of love, lured her proud mate away from the race and distracted him with her femininity.

"Gratefully, we moved on to the second event, the casting of Lugh's spear, which, legend has it, was able to go further than a wind which could encircle the Earth in moments. This was the same spear stolen at one time by the Evil One and placed in the hands of the Roman soldier who used it to pierce Christ's side, the same spear in the Grail legends carried by one of the maidens. Fortunately, these were happier days. By the rules of the contest, Yurigel still had to hurl the spear of Lugh farther than anyone else. However, since all his fellow contestants were either lost in the woods, hanging from tree branches by their hair, or trying to disentangle their feet from tree roots, there were no contestants left but he to throw the great spear of Lugh.

"Still, on that bright sunny day in the green, green field, my beloved and brave Yurigel stood with the spear of Lugh in his hands. On his face was a look of grim determination as he prepared to cast the spear. His mighty arm muscles flexed in tense anticipation, and, with a short run, he cast the spear into the sky. Higher and higher it rose, and then it passed out of our sight until, like a falling star, we saw it fall toward the Earth and disappear somewhere in the vast foliage of the trees. Yurigel, by this time, was feeling quite self-confident about his abilities."

"Well, how could I not?" asked Yurigel. "Except for the King of the Unicorns, I had had no competition up until that point."

"He strutted about the field," said Niamh, "flexing his muscles again and rearranging his bright red hair into a proper topknot upon his head. Since we had made peace between ourselves, with a great flash of his white teeth, he would give me a rogue's smile, and his flashing green eyes held a promise of intimate, romantic mischief. Then it came time for the third contest, which was, if you remember, that my lovely Yurigel had to leap higher than the great Salmon of Wisdom. Now you would think this would not be too difficult a feat. However, the reason that the great Salmon of Wisdom was so grand at leaping was that the Salmon, after many thousands of years, had learned to leap higher and higher, ever so much higher, to be able to grasp the great hazelnuts of wisdom and pluck them from the overhanging limbs of the hazel trees, which stretch across many of the streams, sacred wells, and sacred lakes in our realm. To make it even more difficult, Yurigel had to swim out to the middle of the lake where his feet could not touch the earth. Here he would tread water, and the mighty Salmon would swim up next to him."

"The Salmon had a twinkle in his eye," said Yurigel, "and he was smiling broadly at me, and I thought perhaps he was thinking he was about to teach me a lesson this day. A bit of discomfort began to sneak past my strong walls of self-confidence, but I quickly closed ranks and pushed that small shred of doubt away, placing my focus on what was ahead, which was to leap higher than the Salmon of Wisdom."

"What added even more tension to this affair," Niamh remarked, "was that I noticed my scarf, though still high above the ground, was beginning to drift ever so slowly toward Mother Earth's gentle face. The scarf, in fact, was slowly descending over the lake itself, where my beloved Yurigel was treading water next to the great Salmon of Wisdom."

"Looking up," said Yurigel, "I saw my precious treasure Niamh's scarf slowly circling downward like a leaf, caught up by the wind a bit higher and then falling a little bit lower as it slowly spiraled down towards us. It was then, as I saw the scarf drift closer and closer, that I knew the final contest was near. Treading water, I felt the Salmon twirl beside me, and, with a mighty leap, we both cleared the water, leaping high, high into the air. We both, however, missed our prize of the descending scarf and fell backwards into the lake with a splash. I knew the scarf was still descending, and it was now a matter of who could break free of the water first and grasp the scarf. We did not mention this earlier, but one of the rules of the contest was that I had to grasp the scarf in my mouth, as would the Salmon. We fought our way back up to the surface of the water and, both in synchronicity, broke free of the boundaries of the water, leapt high in the air, and missed again. I tumbled backwards, but this time, the Salmon was tumbling a bit higher than I was, and he landed on my chest and drove me under water.

"Now the Salmon was not cheating, for he is a fair and just player, but he had leapt so high, he had gone off course, and down he fell on me, and down we plunged deeper into the water. Once again, we finally touched the bottom and began the push-off and speeding toward the surface of the lake, each one of us trying to move a few inches ahead of the other. As we spun up toward the surface of the water, we actually wrestled with each other, Elf and Salmon trying to get past each other. The Salmon, having more experience than me by many years, managed to break free of the water ahead of me, though I was close behind. My last leap was one of sheer desperation, for the Salmon was ahead of me, but I felt the energy coursing through me, and I would not give up. With my arms pinned to my sides and my feet held together, I tried to imagine myself a Salmon, but this time what I tried to grasp was even more precious before my eyes than the hazelnut of wisdom. It was the fair scarf of my beloved Niamh, and I saw the scarf descending directly toward the Salmon's gaping mouth. I knew in my heart that he was to grasp the scarf first, and I wondered if my lovely Niamh would be happy wedded to a Salmon, though, in our realm, that is not so strange as it sounds.

"Just as he was about to lock onto the scarf, a wind blew it out of his mouth and over in my direction, and then it was as if he abruptly broke off from his jump and spun backwards to the surface of the lake. The scarf came to me, I grasped it within my jaws, and then I, too, plunged to the surface of the lake. With a splash, I entered deep into the pond. Within those waters, I saw the Salmon come up to me, and he was smiling. All is possible in Tír na nÓg, if you remember, and the Salmon winked at me the way only a Salmon can wink and followed me as I swam my way back to the surface of the lake and to my cherished Niamh.

"Though the humble Salmon would never tell me, I learned the truth a few days later from a Sprite, who lives within a small community of Sprites in the caves behind the waterfall that flowed into the lake. She told me that the Salmon, though he thought my Niamh quite stunning, was much too grand a gentleman to break anyone's heart, especially that of a beautiful woman. Though the scarf was to be his prize, as he drew near it, he blew the scarf in my direction with the breath from his own mouth. Then he broke his own ascent and plunged back to the surface of the lake, thereby allowing me to ascend above him and catch the scarf in my own mouth. Therefore, I, myself, had inadvertently eaten a hazelnut of wisdom. My youthful arrogance passed somewhat away, and I began to see myself, and the way I presented myself to all Creation, a bit more clearly.

"Out of the water I trudged, soaking wet, my fine garments hanging uncomfortably on me, and the scarf lying limp and dripping water from my mouth."

Continued Niamh, "Lake ferns in your hair, you strolled up to me, my champion, my love. You took the scarf from out from your mouth, and you knelt down before me, and you said, 'I humbly ask you, my fair lady, to take this scarf from my unworthy hands, for now I realize I have mistreated you and do not deserve your love. But if you will consider bequeathing your love to me, I will enfold you in my arms and keep you safe. You will be the only star in heaven's nighttime sky for me, and I will see no other. You will be the very breath that gives me life and the light of my eyes that gives me sight. I will love you forever until time ceases to exist and then for an eternity beyond that. I pledge this before the Holy Parents, Christ, and Mary.'

"What could I do? I declared him my champion there and then. I bequeathed my love to him, and we became, in the eyes of those around us, sacred mates, not yet married in a Human sense, but at least promised to one another."

Chapter VIII

The Sprites

We will speak now with two Sprites, Mira Hummingbird, and her sacred mate, Gwionbach Dragonfly. They are the queen and king of the Sprite kingdom in Tír na nÓg. Sprites are among the smallest of the Faerie, standing perhaps three inches in height. Mira has long blonde hair that flows down below her waist. Two golden braids encompass her youthful, beautiful, heart-shaped face. Her compassionate brown eyes, like those of all Fair Folk, are tilted upwards. Her nose is small and well formed, and her lips are full and prone to smile often. From her back sprout four wings the color of stained glass windows, which flutter with her every gesture, or with their own accord, much like a cat's twitching tail. Like all Sprites, she tends to shy away from any form of clothing, except for the occasional leaf or flower hat or scarf. Even such minimal clothing is worn only for a very brief time, as Sprites find clothing quite restrictive. For the moment, Mira has graciously clothed her slender and well-formed figure in a thin, gossamer robe of blue. Her sacred love, Gwionbach, sits beside her.

Gwionbach's appearance, like all Sprites, is angelic in nature. His form brings to mind Michelangelo's statue of David, for his features are without flaw. His light brown halo of hair is curly and flows downwards to rest between his shoulder blades. Gwionbach jokes that if his hair were as long as Mira's, he would constantly entangle it in the limbs of trees. His upward-slanted eyes are golden brown. His nose is strongly formed, and his full lips, like those of his mate Mira, are always to be found laughing or smiling above his square, dimpled chin. In fact, I have never seen a female Sprite who did not have dimples in her cheeks or a male Sprite who did not have a dimple in his chin. Gwionbach, too, has temporarily clothed himself in a gossamer robe of green. His four wings are presently shimmering with the color of sunlight passing through spring's green leaves.

Mira begins, "We are the Sprites. We are the same folk who, a scant hundred years ago, came to the attention of the people of the Victorian age. For a brief time, Humans believed in us, but then, sadly, because the people of your age wish scientific truth, the faith of the people of that time, and especially of this time, faded away. Silly Humans—you believe in Angels, do you not? Do you require a picture of them to believe in their existence? I, Mira Hummingbird, Queen of the Sprites, wish to remind you that many unseen beings walk among you and come in contact with you on a daily basis. I promise you that those iron eyelids of yours will one day be flung suddenly open, and you will see the truth.

"We, the Sprite people, have existed since long, long before your Victorian age. When our Mother Earth was a mere babe in the arms of the Mother and Father Creator, we were born. Their bright light emanated from our bodies as we flew among the trees and flowers and along the newborn grassy slopes. Even before animals were created, we existed. At night, we were the tiny stars that skimmed along the peaceful waters of Mother Earth. After our birth were born the Dragons. I well remember the great Dragons sweeping from the skies. They were, at that time, not the most cognitive creatures of Creation; yet, with their newfound awareness and their great jaws and massive claws, they tried without success to catch us in mid-flight, much like a cat attempting to catch a small flying insect.

"At that time in Creation, we were more energy than physical form. It was not until the creation of the Faerie races, which included the Humans, that we took our bodily shapes as we appear now. You see, we reflect what our parents look like, the Mother and Father Creator. You might say that we were very cognitive embryos with wings, fluttering through the sky. Then, with the birth of Human and Fair Folk, we took on the appearance that the world now understands us to hold. We have had this physical appearance since long, long, long before your civilizations were born. We are sparks of light who reflect the love of our Mother and Father Creator and brother Jesus. We do not exist outside of them, and we cannot exist without them, just as you Humans cannot exist outside of them or without them.

"We have seen our dear Mother Earth pass through many changes, from a toddler to a young girl to a maiden and to the Mother she is now. In the beginning, the Mother and Father and our beloved Jesus walked the Earth, and all was green and bright. The skies were clear, and the fragrance of flowers and the shadows of green leaves were everywhere upon the Earth. There was no war, only love; no death, only life; no sickness, only healing. And we lived forever, all of us together.

"We witnessed the great sadness, the time when Humanity turned their backs upon the Mother and Father and struck out upon their own. In the beginning, Humanity lived in harmony with Mother Earth, but millennium after millennium passed, and we saw their need to live harmoniously with all things slowly change. The Humans felt they had become too filled with wisdom. They lost the innocence the Mother and Father gave to them as their heritage. Then abruptly, within the space of just a few hundred years, Humanity, within their own minds, became lords of the Earth, conquerors, dictators, usurpers of the Mother and Father, claiming that they were the rulers of all Creation. We tried to speak to our Human brothers and sisters, pleading with them to turn back and ask forgiveness of the Holy Family. We tried to help them understand they were not gods, and that they needed the companionship of the Mother and Father Creator, so that their spirits would thrive and their existence on Mother Earth would be lived in harmony and beauty. We pleaded with them to ask forgiveness for their hard-hearted arrogance and their belief that they were superior to all Creation and an equal of the Mother and Father Creator, but Humanity did not heed our pleas.

"Many millennia later, history once again repeated itself, and others of the Fair Folk, those who would later become known as Gnomes, Elves, and many of the other Fair Folk tribes, decided that they, too, did not need the constant guidance of the Mother and Father Creator in their lives. Like their Human brothers and sisters, they, too, left the Garden. Again, our pleas went unheeded, and, with great sadness, we watched our Faerie brothers and sisters march out of Eden, or Tír na nÓg.

"In anguish, we flew to our Mother and Father Creator. Standing upon their knees and resting gently upon their open palms, in great sorrow, we wept and pleaded with them to call back our Faerie family. We could not bear the loss of those who were so close to us in nature, for we still grievously mourned the passing of our Human family many, many millennia before. The Mother and Father Creator wiped away our tears, but they told us that all of their children had free will. They said that the Humans and the Faerie had made the decision to leave their presence and set out upon their own pathway, which would lead them far from their true heart's home. To ease our sorrow, they promised us they would always watch over their children and would send our Angel family to watch over our Human and Faerie families. One day, they told us, our big brother (who would later become known to the world as Jesus) would come to Mother Earth and be born in a Human body. Through his love and sacrifice, he would provide a pathway, so that the Fair Folk and Humans might find their way home to the Mother and Father Creator and back to Tír na nÓg.

"We Sprites, before our Mother and Father and before our loving big brother, Jesus, asked if it would be possible that we, like the Angels, could be given the ability to travel between the worlds of spirit and the more physical world of Mother Earth where our families had fled. We asked this of them that we might still be able to plead with our Faerie and Human families to return home. Even though they had not listened to our counsel while we were in the presence of the Mother and Father, we hoped that eventually, with our determined persistence (and I do say that we are the very gnats of persistence), our families would hear our words and turn their hearts back to the Mother and Father. The Mother and Father and Jesus gladly gave us permission to carry out our mission, so that we and other spirit companions and all living things of Mother Earth, including all animals and green things and stone things and all the rest of Mother Earth's children, would act as counselors to our Human and Faerie families.

"Happily, others of our Faerie family heeded the Mother and Father's call first and, over many millennia, began their journey back home to the Mother and Father and Jesus, back home to their beloved Tír na nÓg. Sadly, Humanity has been rather stubborn, but we do find, especially within these last few years, that Humans are beginning to awaken. Like their Faerie family before them, some Humans are turning their eyes back to their spiritual home of the heart, back to the Mother and Father Creator. My beloved Human brothers and sisters, the Garden is not gone. Open your eyes and look around you. It is still here. Break free of your stubborn, self-inflicted imprisonment, and understand the way back to the Garden is where you are standing, and you are already there. Allow yourself to become aware of it."

"Perhaps," began Gwionbach, "some of you may wonder what influence tiny beings like us can have on our environment or on other areas within Creation. Well, besides enjoying life to the fullest through singing, playing, feasting, and visiting with our own kind and others of the Fair Folk, we also have duties that are more serious. These duties include helping the Gnomes and others of the Fair Folk to care for plants and animals in your physical world. We act as observers of what is happening in the physical world, so that we may report back what we have seen in your world, both good and bad, to the Faerie tribes in our realm and to the Mother and Father themselves. We also sometimes come in direct contact with Humans in the physical realm and act, unbeknownst to them, as tiny advisors or counselors. In other words, when we come upon a Human about to commit an act that could result in damage to our Mother Earth or one of her children, we try to persuade that person to change his or her mind. We do not always have the ability to sway a spiritually unbalanced Human from evil intentions, for sadly we are often simply ignored. I will speak of one instance, however, where we participated directly in the prevention of a battle between two Celtic tribes.

"The actual reason for the conflict between these tribes was that a young man of one tribe had fallen in love with a young woman of a different tribe. Now the brother to the young man was pleased at his brother's choice of the young woman to be his bride, but the brother of the young woman was not so pleased, for he had a keen interest in encouraging her to marry another man who happened to be the chieftain of their own tribe. By marrying this chieftain, the young woman would not only bring prestige to her family, but she would bring an elevated position of power and wealth to her brother. I should inform you, of course, that the young woman and the young man of the other tribe loved each other very much, while the young woman herself wanted nothing to do with the chieftain of her own tribe.

"The wishes of the young woman's brother regarding her marriage to the chieftain were thwarted, at first, by the decision of the local Druids. Perhaps you have heard that many Druids had a gift of the ability to look far into the future to see what was best for the people they served. The Druids, in this instance, decided that the young woman would best be suited to marry the young man, since this would bring more prosperity to both tribes in the years to come.

"The chieftain of the young woman's tribe and her brother could not openly disagree with the decision of the Druids. Therefore, they went out one day, slaughtered three of their tribe's pigs, and took the pigs' remains to the area of the other tribe, where they left them. The chieftain then returned home, gathered his tribe together, and informed them that three of their pigs were missing. He forced the frightened farmer who owned the three missing pigs to declare that he saw the young man of the other tribe steal the pigs. The chieftain, with the help of the frightened pig farmer, led a group of his warriors to the area of the other tribe and showed them the carcasses of the pigs. Then, before all assembled, the chieftain declared that they must receive compensation from the tribe for the theft of the pigs. He claimed that a fair compensation for the theft and slaughter of the pigs would be thirty cattle.

"The chieftain next sent one of his warriors with his petition to the chieftain of the other tribe, where the warrior flung the accusation of the false crime in the chieftain's face. The chieftain did not believe the accusation, for he knew that the young man was honest and trustworthy, and he had been within sight of other witnesses from his own tribe throughout the day. Knowing this, the honest chieftain declared that his tribe was not about to turn over thirty head of cattle to a tribe of liars and thieves. At that point, the messenger who carried the false accusation formally declared to the honest chieftain that the next morning, the warriors of both tribes would meet upon the field of battle. There they would decide this matter of thievery, that the gods might decide the true thief and liar. The false chieftain was certain that the young man of the other tribe would fight in the battle the next day. He believed that the brother of the young woman would kill the young man, for he had assigned the brother the role of assassin. Otherwise, the chieftain thought, he himself would kill the young man with his own sword. Therefore, the beautiful young woman would have no choice but to marry the false chieftain.

"The Celtic people of that time, primarily due to superstition, would never wage a battle at night, but would begin the battle at first dawn the next day. We Sprites had witnessed all that had passed, and we had also thoroughly questioned the other witnesses (in this case, mostly animals and the other pigs who were kin to the slain pigs). We had learnt the truth of the evil intent of the chieftain and the young woman's brother. The two opposing armies marched to a large, green meadow and began to strategically stake out the best place to set up their camps, so that, in their minds, they would have the best vantage point from which to wage their battle. Now we knew, beyond a shadow of a doubt, that warriors on the eve of a battle would not take the least heed of our counsel. Therefore, we gathered our court together, and we devised our own strategy, in a bold attempt to disrupt the battle before it began.

"Many of the men in both camps slept beneath the open sky, wrapped in their blankets and surrounding their cooking fires, while the chieftains and those of higher rank slept in various sized tents. Around both camps, guards were placed to ensure that the enemy camp did nothing underhanded during the night. Though the guards of both camps keeping watch were alert and highly motivated by the battle to take place on the coming morning, we Sprites, unseen by them, sang a lullaby song, so that all the watchful guards in both camps collapsed, almost as one, into sleeping heaps of sweet dreams.

"That task completed, my troops flitted about the camp and the forms of the sleeping men, whispering into their sleeping ears peaceful and loving thoughts about the men in the other camp. We whispered words such as, why would two such dear friends as you are wish to hack each other to death with swords. Would it not be more pleasant to meet on the field upon the morrow to do battle with cups of mead, and let the champion be the last man standing with his cup in his hand? We found that some of the men were more stubborn than others, so we put into their minds loving thoughts of their enemies who rested across from them in the other camp— images of them holding each other's hands as they skipped among the flowers in the meadow. We found that some of the men took our lessons a bit too much to heart the next day, but at least they did not kill one another.

"The chieftains were more troublesome. We whispered in the honest chieftain's ear the suggestion that he withdraw his men and take the matter to the Druids. Let the Druids use their power of farsight to see the truth of what really happened with the slaughter of the three pigs. Sadly, however, this chieftain, even in his dreams, was focused on the battle the next day and would not take our counsel. He considered that to withdraw his men would be a cowardly retreat, and that the honor of his tribe and himself were at stake. Even with our strongest magical influence, he rejected the image of himself holding hands and skipping through the meadow with the other chieftain (although we did not really think that would work anyway).

"We did not wish to cause dishonor to this chieftain, for he was a good man, not only to his wife and children, but also to his tribe. Next, we gave him a dream where he would play peacefully and happily with his young children in the very same meadow where the battle was to take place, for he loved his children very much and would often play with them, even though he was a great warrior. He seemed to take pleasure in this dream, though he still tried to return to his dreams of the field of battle. We continued to cause him to return to his dream of playing with his children, and then, seeing the pleasure he received from this dream, we lengthened it yet a bit more. He did not wake until very late the next day and only awoke then when one of his men, waking from his own dream, came to rouse him.

"Now the other chieftain and the young brother were much harder to deal with in their dreams, so great was the chieftain's lust for the brother's young sister and so great was the young brother's lust for wealth and power. They resisted all of the peaceful dreams with which we tried to enchant them. The evil chieftain was dreaming of slaughtering the young woman's loved one and ravishing her afterwards, while the young brother was dreaming of sitting upon a throne even more lavish than the chieftain's with great wealth in the form of gold coins, jewelry, crowns, shields, armor, and people bowing before him. Even the chieftain was there in his dream, kneeling before him.

"So persistent were we with the chieftain, whispering in his ear, that he began to dream of us as gnats bothering him, so that, in his sleep, he would raise his arm to brush us away or try to squash us between his hands. So much did we trouble him that we were obliged to spend most of the night artfully dodging his blows. We flitted here and there about his hands, many times coming close to being squashed between them. The more he tried to squash us, the more menacing we became in his dreams. No longer were we ants, but great, angry bees, and, in his dreams, he was trying to swat at us and keep us from stinging him.

"We realized that we were finally having an effect on him, so, in his dreams, we made ourselves into very large, angry bees. Each of us, as a bee in his dreams, was about the size of his head, and we had great, massive stingers. We would buzz and fly all about him and sting him on various parts of his body, particularly upon his rump. Normally, we are not this cruel, but we had to do something to stop the battle. So vigorous did we become in our stinging of the chieftain in his dreams that he abruptly woke from his sleep, saw our buzzing forms around him, flung off his bed sheets, and fled from his tent out into the night. We chased him for many miles until he collapsed in an exhausted heap beside a stream, where we left him, although some of us stayed behind in the woods around him, making loud, angry, buzzing noises until the break of the next day.

"Now, in the brother's dream, not only were people bowing to him, but they were bringing him treasure and laying it at his feet. We quickly real-ized that this resonated most closely with his spirit in his dream. It brought him great pleasure to have bags of gold and jewels poured at his feet, so we became people in his dream who poured bags of gold upon his lap. He began to laugh and laugh, and he laughed even harder when even more gold was poured upon his lap, so that we brought an endless parade of people pouring large bags of gold upon him. He continued with his merriment until he began to realize that he was to be buried alive by gold. Though he commanded us to stop, we, as his faithful, loyal servants, could not bring ourselves to stop bringing him treasure. We continued to heap upon him all forms of gold and jewelry until, in his dream, only his head rose above the great mound of treasure. There, with his head rising just above the treasure, he pleaded with us to stop, but we told him that we loved him so much, and he was such a great ruler, that we had to bring him more treasure to show our esteem for him.

"The young brother struggled mightily and finally broke free from the mound of gold, but still we would not stop bringing him bags of gold and jewels. We had so many more to pour over him that, in order to spare his life, he did the only thing he could do. He fled his loyal servants and their large bags of treasure. He, like his chieftain, woke abruptly from his dream and tried to flee his small tent, though he at first believed his tent to be a large bag of gold from which he could not escape until we showed him the opening. He fled into the night, while, behind him, we continued to create for him the illusion of his many loyal servants running desperately after him to share with him their love and their esteem, chasing him for many miles in the opposite direction from his chieftain. He finally collapsed upon a hill that rose slightly above the forest, and there, beneath the hill, we caused our voices to ring out as his loyal servants, calling for him to show himself, so that we, in our esteem, might bring him more treasure, until he finally fell into an exhausted sleep upon the break of day.

"The next day, late in the afternoon, both camps of men finally awoke from their dreams. Upon leaving his tent, the honest chieftain discovered the men of both camps sitting closely together, engaging in drinking contests. Even stranger to the chieftain's eye, however, was the sight of men from both camps holding hands as they wandered through the meadow of flowers. It appeared that no one was interested in war that day. When he questioned the men of the other camp, he learned that the evil brother and the chieftain had fled during the night and were now considered cowards by their own men. The honest chieftain had no choice but to join in the merriment, which continued until late in the evening of that same day. We are happy to say that the good fellowship continued for many years into the future, and eventually the tribes united as one.

"As the Druids had prophesied, the young man and the young woman in their marriage brought great wealth and prestige, honor, and wisdom to both tribes. The young man became chieftain later, after the honest chieftain's death, and the young woman, his bride, became his chieftess and queen. The two ruled the people of both tribes with fairness, honor, and great wisdom.

"Later on that day, the dishonest chieftain and the brother were found by Druids, who by then had learned from us the truth of what had really happened to the three slaughtered pigs. These noble Druids made switches from birch and drove the chieftain and the deceitful brother deep into the woods and away from their communities. There were some rumors that later on, in another part of the land, far from their old homes, the two men became unsuccessful bandits. The chieftain, to the very end of his short life, had a terrible fear of bees and would not partake of anything containing honey, not even mead. The deceitful brother gave up his bandit ways, for he could not tolerate the feel of gold or any other form of wealth, and he later became a hermit in a cave. So ends the story of the dishonest chieftain and the deceitful brother."

The Brownies

The Brownies are somewhat shorter than the Gnomes, standing perhaps a foot in height. They cannot bear to enter Human dwellings due to the energy waves that flow constantly from our appliances and machines. Two very brave Brownies dared to enter our home, so that we could record their words here.

"I am Greta Flowerfriend, and my mate or husband is Jack Surefoot. We are two of the Brownies about whom Humans have, for countless ages, made up tales. I am sure you have heard of us. The Wee Folke, they call us, the ones who dance under the full moon in a ring of mushrooms. Always dancing, we are, always feasting in the moonlight, out in the deepest part of the forest, until some unwary Human stumbles upon our celebration. Then he must suddenly pay the price for finding us by dancing the night away or being spirited away to one of our great halls beneath the hill. Even worse, he might be dragged along by his ears as we fly upwards, carrying him high, high into the night sky with us. You have heard these stories, I am sure, and I am sorry to say a few of them are quite true.

"We are scattered throughout the realms. We do not live in the dark realms; this physical realm is the closest we get to the dark realms. Some strange cousins of ours do dwell in the dark realms, but they are so different from us that we are no longer even of the same tribe. No, my people live in Mother Earth's physical realm and in the realms beyond, which move gently toward the Mother and Father Creator. We are especially scattered throughout Tír na nÓg, where we are left unmolested by uninvited guests, and any outsiders who visit our celebrations are personally welcomed by us. Yes, it is true some Humans have had unfortunate encounters with us in the past, but the truth of the matter is, though we might have scared them off, we have never, ever really hurt anyone, contrary to what your stories may say. We only wished them to leave us in peace, for we do not wish to harm anyone.

"Why are we so protective of our gatherings? Well, in years long past, Humans did not have our best interests at heart. There have been too many Humans who tried purposely to stomp on us with their great, big feet or to snatch us and exhibit us at their fairs for some coins. Like our poor Leprechaun cousins, they sometimes grabbed us and tried to force us to tell them where we had hidden our riches. Again, to shed new light upon the legend of Brownies, we, like many of the Leprechauns, have no riches in which Humans would be interested. Many times, Humans would approach us unannounced, so that they could watch our celebrations. That was not so bad if they did not bother us, but it seems Humans, of the past anyway, always had some intent to take something from us, even the very songs that we sang among ourselves.

"We must be honest, however, and tell you there have also been encounters with Humans that were welcome. We, the tribes of the Brownies, have taught many of your Human musicians our songs and how better to play their instruments. Through the gift of Brownie magic, these potential musicians became renowned throughout their land. You see, music is our treasure. All of us are musicians, singers, and dancers, and that is pretty much how we spend our time.

"Now you would think that we little people are quite a lazy lot. You see, our gift from the Mother and Father, and from our beloved brother Jesus, and from our delightful and ever beautiful Mother Mary Earth, is to create positive energy through musical instruments, song, and dance. You see, the Gnomes, the larger ones of our family, tend directly to ailing plants and sick animals. They are what you would call the front line of battlefield doctors for the Mother's children, or for all Creation. We, on the other hand, are more the bards of Creation. Through our music, by instrument and song and dance, we raise the energy (or the aura or vibration or whatever word you wish to use) of the area we dwell in.

"If a creek or stream has become gloomy due to natural or manmade causes, we ease the stream's torment and the darkness or possible malevolence of the area by the gift of music and by our frenzied dancing. We feel the Mother and Father have given us a wonderful gift, for we do love to dance, sing, and play instruments. That is our form of prayer, and, by doing this, we help bring more light into a darkened area. Many of our songs are praise songs to the Mother and Father and Jesus and to Mother Mary. Many of our songs are story songs, and many of our songs are cheerful spirit songs. We speak in a tongue known only to us and a few other Fair Folk. Not many can speak it as fluently as we can, for it is a tongue given to us directly by the Mother and Father Creator. We call it the healing tongue.

"You will find us in the more remote areas, though they are becoming far and few in your physical world. We do spend much of our time in your gardens and even in the flower boxes of those who dwell in green-less cities. Wherever life exists, be it animal, plant, or even Human, you will find us there. You will find us even in the more populated areas where there is little nature, but our homes are ever in realms not of the physical, so that, at night, we may live peacefully among the great, green places of Tír na nÓg and other Faerie realms of light. It is also true that you can find us many times dancing within a Faerie ring of mushrooms, for we feel that that is a direct request or sign from the Mother and Father or Jesus that they wish us to dance there—that there we are to hold our celebration. Now I think I will rest and let my beloved Jack carry on the tale from here."

"Well," Jack began, "let us talk about the proper etiquette upon discovering a Brownie celebration and how you, as a Human, should approach said celebration without causing undue distress to us or to yourself. The first thing to keep in mind is that very few Humans ever see one of our celebrations, and for you to even set your eyes upon such a thing is surely a gift from the Mother and Father and their beloved son and should not be taken lightly. That is how one always gets in trouble, by taking the gifts of the Holy Family lightly and stepping in the wrong place at the wrong time. Then we leave little reminders to help you to have more respect for mysteries that come from the Mother and Father and Jesus.

"Let us say, then, that you have set your eyes upon us in the midst of our rabblerousing and in the midst of our songs and dancing and laughter. Should you be drunk, just say a little prayer and slowly back away from us, and go about your way. Perhaps when you get home under your own roof, you might ask the Mother and Father for another chance. I am not saying you should give up the drink, but I am saying to drink more responsibly, so at least you can walk on your own feet and not fall face first into one of our celebrations, which has happened, you know. I cannot tell you how many times, over my long lifespan, some drunken Human has staggered up to one of our celebrations, eyes full of wonder, and then, dancing a clumsy jig, has fallen face first upon our celebration, scattering all of us here and there, hither and yon. I wish to tell you now, and I want it to be known, that, as the drunkard lay face-first upon the ground, he received many tiny boot kicks on his posterior for his disgraceful behavior.

"Now, on the other hand, if you have come across us, and you are sober as a saint, I would say you have two choices. Say a little prayer to the Mother and Father, perhaps thanking them for showing you a mystery that night. Then, if you feel uncomfortable, continue on your way, and do not disturb us. However, if you feel the need to make your presence known to us, because that need is set upon you by the Mother and Father or by Jesus or by some saint, then sit down upon the ground where you first saw us, wait a spell, keep silent, and we will notice you at some point.

"If we tend to ignore you, you might perhaps say a very polite, 'Excuse me, please, my good ladies and gentlemen, I wish to join in the celebration with you.' If we look upon you and your heart is sincere (and we can see your heart, how sincere it is—we can read your thoughts), we will invite you to join our fun, our celebration, so that you, with us, the Brownies, can also become a healer of the land. Merlin wonders whether we keep the Humans their normal size as they dance about us, or do we shrink them down to our size. It depends upon the mood of the Human and our mood. Some we shrink down to our size, because they ask it, while some wish to remain their normal size. That is fine with us, for, when they dance to our music, they receive the gift of grace, so they can watch their feet and where they place them.

"Depending upon the reason the Holy Family has brought you to us, we may be moved by them to give you a gift. These gifts come in different packages. One gift may be that you become, like us, musical healers, and travel about the land bringing light and chasing away the darkness. It may be that you receive the gift of sight, so that, from that point on, you will be able to see us, the little people, and others of the Fair Folk. It may be the gift of far-sight, or seeing in to the future, the past, or even into your own present time a little bit more clearly. One gift may be that you learn to travel between the realms and travel the Faerie lands as a welcome guest.

"The most wonderful gift of all, at least in our opinion (and understand that we do not give this gift unless we are told to do so by the Mother, Father, and Jesus), is to give the gift of all of these things—music, Faery sight, farsight, and the gift of the Faery traveler—to one person. Still, to be given any one of these gifts, and most especially the last gift, is a great responsibility given to you by the Mother, Father, and Jesus, and it must not be abused. I just tell you this because you may find it interesting. It does not mean it will ever happen to you. It does not mean you will receive any one of these gifts, or that you will ever see us at all. Just the same, I think all of us, whether we be Brownie or others of the Faerie lands, do openly and secretly share one hope. Our hope is that you do learn to see us, so that this realm you call the physical realm can finally begin its road to healing, which will be completed upon the return of our beloved Jesus to our beloved Mother Earth and to the rest of us in Creation.

"One little fact you may find interesting is that the best musician, the best singer, the best healer, the best dancer, and the best at any other gift you can imagine is our beloved brother, Jesus. Especially I want to point out to you that he dances. It is hard not to dance with joy in the presence of the Mother and Father. I just wanted to bring this to your attention, you Humans who never dance, so that perhaps the realization of this fact, this truth that I bring to you, that Jesus dances, will so transform your lives that you will get up at this very moment to dance in celebration to honor the Mother and Father and to honor Jesus. Remember, another famous dancer was King David. He loved to dance, and he was a fine musician.

"To aid you, dear reader, in identifying us when you come upon us, so that you do not mistake us for someone else, here is the general physical description of a Brownie. We usually range in height, using your form of measurement, from about a foot to fifteen or sixteen inches tall. There is a giant for you! Like all Fair Folk, we have the pointy ears that tilt downward at the tips like the Gnomes. Physically, we appear as a slender people. If we appear potbellied, it is because we have small objects tucked away in our tunics or jackets, objects we have collected along the way.

"Some of us wear clothing; some of us do not. A Brownie's choice to wear clothing or not to wear clothing is due to personal preference and not always due to the area in which they dwell. Whether a Brownie chooses to wear clothing or not (and that decision may change from day to day), you will always find a Brownie with a bag upon his or her shoulder, which can be referred to as the Brownie Bag. This bag contains some musical instrument of our choice and little odds and ends we pick up along the way, plus our lunch or supper, whatever food we carry along with us. We do travel, sometimes many miles away from our home, but we always come back home. We have lived for millennia in many of the homes in which we now dwell. In our journeys to heal the land, we tend to travel upon consistent routes, and so we become responsible for certain areas. We try to keep them as cheerful as possible, though I am sorry to say that is becoming more difficult in this day and age of Humanity.

"Our homes are always to be found in the ground, often beneath the roots of a tree or on the side of a bank or along the rolling grassy hills. I am very proud to say that the few Humans who do visit our homes beneath the earth are quite impressed with the high estate of their civilized nature, for they are not dark, dank holes in the ground. We take pride in our homes and tend to have rooms filled with comfy, cozy furniture, musical instruments, and books, and, very importantly, well-stocked larders and large kitchens. Of course, we also have large, comfortable bedrooms and even larger greeting rooms (or what you would call living rooms), where we can talk with our guests. We love light, so, in our realm, our cozy little holes in the ground have a nice assortment of windows to let the light in, and large round doors that are flung open upon the approach of any welcome guest. On cold nights, we always have a great fire roaring in the fireplace, and we love to sit on the hearth in front of it. Even when it is summer, we sit around at the hearth and talk.

"We do partake in Brownie fairs and, of course, the fairs held by the other Fair Folk. Anywhere a celebration is being held, be it Fair Folk or even be it Human, you will find Brownies celebrating right along with you. Still, in all honesty, we do not always attend Human fairs. Although we love to partake of the drink and the food, Human celebrations tend to go too far. At a moment's notice, a pleasant celebration can turn quite unpleasant. Who wants to attend a party like that, may I ask you?

"Now, Greta, my beloved, my bright shining star, my golden leaf, the moonlight of my life, the sunlight of my morning, will carry on from here."

Greta continues, "The final conversation we will have, our new and curious friends, will be a description of us. As Jack has clearly stated, we are of a slender nature and of a short stature, at least to you. Our skin color could be anything from very brown-skinned to very fair-skinned. Our hair colors vary from the typical Human colors of black, blonde, or red (many of us have red hair) to any Human hair color you can think of. It should be mentioned that a few of us do have hair of blue and hair of green and other colors you may find in nature. We have not seen anyone with purple hair, although that is a good color for hair. We can always choose to change our hair color, but usually we are happy with the color we choose early in life.

"Like all Fair Folk, we have a youthful appearance. Unlike most other Fair Folk, however, when we are grown, though our bodies take on the appearance of an adult, our facial features retain more of a childlike inno-cence, perhaps somewhat like the face of an eight or nine year old child. Our ears, as remarked upon earlier, have the downward-tipped points, our eyes are slanted as is favored by most Fair Folk, and we usually have quite a lot of hair on our heads. Many of us braid our hair and wear it in different, elaborate hairstyles, in whatever mood takes us. Many times, we let it hang freely and do what it wishes, when it is not becoming tangled around a bush. The men also tend to have long hair. Even the ones who wear it shorter tend to have lots and lots of it. I have known no Brownie who has had short hair above or around the ears. It is usually at least down to the shoulders. A few of our men do grow beards or mustaches. Imagine a little boy, eight or nine years old, with a beard. Now that might look, depending upon the boy, quite adorable. Most people would think it was not a real beard or mustache, and that is how our male Brownies look if they grow a beard or mustache; yet, still, you would find them quite striking.

"Merlin has asked us now to describe ourselves. My beloved Jack has dark brown hair, blue eyes, and fair skin. His hair is quite curly. He has curls everywhere. He is the most curly-haired Brownie I have ever known. It is quite becoming on him. Curly waves of hair flow down to his shoulders. His hair, being so thick, sometimes obscures his beautiful, wonderful face, and I have to brush back his hair from his face just to find him again. His eyes are blue as a turquoise sky upon a field of snow. His mouth is large and generous, and, when he smiles, his dimples come out and lend further enchantment to his already quite enchanted face. That is my Jack. Slender of build, but still muscular for a man, he is one of the giants we spoke of earlier—at least sixteen inches tall without his hat."

Jack continues, "My dear Greta is a wee lass. She will be lucky if she reaches twelve inches unless she stands on her tiptoes, as she is prone to do as she dances in the meadows and forest clearings. Her fair hair is the color of sunlight. Her nose is small, like the rest of her delicate facial features, and upon her lovely cheeks are light brown freckles. These capture and tug at your heart when she gives you one of her brilliant smiles, which is quite often, for she is not a miser when it comes to smiles and laughter. Her eyes are as gray as the lovely mist of the early morning. Her slender body is that of a nymph or a goddess. In fact, every time I behold her, I feel my heart's need to worship her and be thankful for her love. My dear Greta also has a unique gift—when she laughs, the tips of her ears begin to wiggle, carrying me upward spiritually in ecstasy with my love for her. There you are, Human. Behold my Greta, and congratulate me for being such a lucky man.

"The time for our little gathering has come to an end, dear reader. From both of us, may you hear the Mother and Father's call to you, may you find Jesus' hand to hold, and may Mother Earth provide you with comfort during your darkest days. May the Angels sing to you, and may you listen to the advice of saints all around you. Walk upon the green way. Farewell, farewell, we may see you again one day. Farewell, my Human friends."

CHAPTER IX

The Centaurs

"We send greetings to all Humankind. I am called Amera Trueheart. I am here with my beloved one, Lugh Strongarm. We are of the Centaur tribe. I would assume many Humans are familiar with us from the Greek myths and from the image of Sagittarius if you have come in contact with astrology. Though it may be hard to believe in our existence, we are more real than you are. In fact, many different tribes of beings are part Human or part Elf and part animal. We are also known by the name of Pookas, beings who change from an Elven form to that of a Horse. If you have read your Greek and Roman legends, you will find stories of us there. A very famous Centaur often featured in your legends is Epona, the horse goddess. Many Centaurs are healers, such as our female cousin, Glee, and her husband, Sherlaw. Lugh and I are not healers, *per se*, though we can be when needed. Instead, we are warriors, clad in full body armor from our Elven torsos to our equine bodies. We are quite proud of our appearance and feel quite blessed to be one part Elf and the other part horse."

We would like to add here a description of Amera and Lugh, so that you will be able to visualize them more clearly. Amera's upper body is that of a beautiful, young Elven woman with long, black flowing hair, slanted eyes the color of a blue sky, pale skin with blushing red cheeks, and full red lips that often form into a mischievous smile. Her equine portion is that of a beautiful, sleek, black horse with a full, thick, black tail. When she walks, her silver hooves sometimes strike sparks from the stones upon the ground. When on soldier duty, her entire Centaur body, Elven and horse, is clad in protective, heavy body armor. When she is off-duty, she may clothe her Elven torso in the type of clothing worn by a young woman of the Renaissance period. Often, however, she prefers to go unclad and bare-breasted, so that when she runs free, she can feel the wind upon her entire body. Her mate, Lugh Strongarm, is taller in stature than Amera, with long, beautiful, golden hair flowing below his shoulders and a close-cropped golden beard upon his face. His Elven eyes are steel-grey in color, and his Elven torso is quite muscular. Like his mate, Amera, he can be found wearing body armor, a bit of clothing on his upper torso, or, as is frequently his preference, no clothing at all.

Lugh remarks, "We are one of the least bashful people of the Faerie world. When the day comes when we walk among you Humans in the physical world, you will just have to get over your prudishness and accept our nakedness, as we stand before you with great smiles upon our faces. I am assuming that will take some adjustment upon your part. Do not fret. We will help you through this period of discomfort, and we will band together as old friends at the feasting table. After you have consumed much of our mead and enjoyed our fine food, our tendency to disrobe will no longer even matter to you, and we will all become great friends."

Amera continues more seriously, "Many uncountable ages ago, beings, whether they were Elven, Human, or animal, did not house their spirits in rigid shapes as they do today. In those days, spirits would flow from shape to shape, sometimes Elf, sometimes Human, sometimes animal, sometimes tree, rock, or even cloud. Our ancestors were a truly free people back then, and all tribes were one. At some point in long forgotten history, spirit beings began to house themselves more frequently in a certain body or shape. After a time, Elves became Elves, Humans became Humans, bears became bears, fish became fish, trees became trees, and so on. There were a few of us, though, who could not quite decide what form we liked best. We debated among ourselves—should we become Elven, should we become animals, a horse, a bear, or another being? We could not decide. This is how Pookas were born—Elven beings who delighted in the physical form of an Elf, but delighted equally in the form of a particular animal.

"Pookas, after a time, tended to develop into sub-tribes, with each tribe focusing on a certain animal. One well-known tribe is, of course, our own, the Centaur tribe. Another tribe equally well known would be the Faun or Pan tribe. These beings are either part Elf or part Gnome, combined with a deer or a goat. Another tribe, very well known to sailors, is the Merpeople. Part Elf and part fish, these beings have been known to bring great pleasure to Humanity or great disaster, in the form of a shipwreck or by pulling men's bodies down to the ocean deeps. Another tribe would be Water Nymphs, very close to the Merpeople. Water Nymphs can be male or female, and they can also take on a Mer appearance. Other Pookas might take on the complete form of an Elf and then frequently shape-shift into that of another animal. Now all Fair Folk are shape-shifters and can take on any appearance they wish, but a true Pooka will remain most of its life in a mixed state, such as that of a Centaur or the animal it is most fond of, such as a bear or a lion, a hound, a wolf, or a bird. The form does not matter—it is whatever form the Pooka feels most comfortable in.

"A consistent theme seems to run through many of the legends of your time concerning Pookas. This oft-repeated tale concerns a poor, unwitting mortal, who, while passing through the deep forest, unexpectedly comes upon a beautiful Faerie horse from the Underworld. Compelled against their will, the man or woman climbs upon the back of this Faerie horse. Suddenly, with the bewildered, trapped Human upon their back, the Faerie horse runs for the deepest body of water, a river or perhaps even the ocean. The Human, unable to leap from the horse's back, is taken into the watery depths and drowned.

"Tales abound of the Water Nymphs or Mermaids, who, with their beautiful songs, lure the poor males to the edge of the water and pull them to their lairs far below. Why do we mention these tales? We want to put the record right again, because the majority of these tales are foolish and one-sided. Pookas also live in the dark realms, and perhaps this is where Humans encountered these deadly enemies. I can fairly say there have been times when Humans have leapt unwanted upon our own backs, especially those of us who choose the form of our lovely ancestral mother, Epona, the horse goddess. The mortal man, and, less frequently, the mortal woman, in their lust to possess a beautiful horse, tries to capture us by stealth or brute force. Of course, if you view it from our side, if you had someone upon your back, you would do everything you possibly could to shake them free. Most of the wild rides upon the Pooka's back ended with Humans being knocked off by tree branches or falling off the Pooka's back onto a bank near some body of water. Very seldom will a Pooka take a life, unless it is in self-defense. You may find that what I have just said ties in with what Lugh, my beloved, wishes to share with you at this point."

Lugh continues, "Like you Humans, we Centaurs have tasks we carry out through the days of our long lives. Our task, Amera's and mine, is that of guards. We are actually soldiers in the Centaur cavalry. Being both Elf and Horse, what other unit would we be in? Our present task is protecting our much loved Merlin and Lili. For many millennia, Amera and I have fought on the front lines in the dark realms against Ogres and Hobgoblins and other dark beings, so our current duty is much more pleasant. We do not come across so many angry Hobgoblins and Trolls in your physical realm. However, that is changing, and more dark beings are crossing over into your physical world. Some of these dark beings retain their own loathsome form, and some merge with the spirits of Humans and, after a time, take control of their bodies. We of the Centaur cavalry have faced these beings many times before over the years, but it is rather disheartening to find more and more of these beings hiding away in Human bodies. Due to our experience and training, it is easy for us and others of the Faerie world to spot them.

"I think, though, that, in some ways, the true task given to us by the Mother and Father and Jesus is to be the in-between people, neither animal nor Elf, but somewhere between the two. Perhaps our presence helps to remind Humanity that their concept of supposedly unyielding, physically unchangeable bodies is nothing more than an illusion, and that, if they wish, they can learn to shape-shift into any form they desire. I think that if Humans learn to live in the physical body that most resonates with their spirit, all Creation will be a much more beautiful and peaceful place. Let me put it this way—no matter what you look like, no matter how your physical body appears to you, it is an illusion. We can see through this illusion, and we see your true body, which resonates in harmony with your spirit, and we wish to tell you that we find you quite beautiful."

Amera adds, "In closing, you may notice a Pooka someday watching you, be it an extremely clever bird or a hound that seems to watch you with eyes of ancient awareness. Perhaps, deep in the forest, you will stumble upon a horse in a clearing that gives you a certain look. I would advise you, before you decide to take any wild rides, to ask permission, so that your experience with that particular Pooka will be an enjoyable one and not another tale of woe to be told later around Human campfires. I think what my beloved Lugh did not point out to you is that, no matter what body we live in, we are all one family, be we Fair Folk or Human or animal or rock or tree or any other of our cousins upon Mother Earth. Because of our fluid, shape-shifting spirits, we are truly one people, and, in reality, we have the ability to learn to walk in another's shoes or hoofs or paws, if you will.

"May the Mother and Father and our beloved brother, Jesus, and our sweet, dear Mother Mary Earth watch out for you, and may you treat all beings you encounter in your life with respect and gentleness. Farewell, Humans. Mother's blessing from two Pookas of the Centaur tribe."

The Merfolk

We will speak now with Demetra and Roth of the Merfolk tribe. Demetra is the niece of Manannán MacLir, Ealilithea's father. Manannán is known as the Sea God among the Celts, while in other cultures he is sometimes referred to as Neptune or Poseidon. Demetra, like all Fair Folk, is quite beautiful. Her complexion is fair, and her features beautifully delicate. Her upper torso is that of a slender, young woman, with long, dark, ringlets of hair flowing gracefully past her shoulders to fall below her waist. Her upward-slanted eyes are of a deep blue, a color reminiscent of the vast sea of which she is a part. She is clad now in a long, sleeveless gown of a shimmering gray material. The gown flows downward over her knees and to her feet, which are bare with distinctive webbing between the toes. Small, delicate fish scales cover her feet, while both her slender legs are covered in these same delicate fish scales. Demetra tells us that Merpeople, when they walk on land, shed their well-known tail and walk on what we would consider Human legs. They can choose to have their legs covered in scales, as Demetra now has, or the lower half of their body can appear as natural as that of another Human. Demetra says that if she was to walk among Humans in the physical world, she would ensure that her body looked entirely Human, though she would retain her Elven facial features and her great beauty.

Roth, her love and mate, would be considered tall for a Human male. His facial features are quite handsome, even beautiful. His hair is of a bright, golden blonde hue, while his upward-tilted eyes are as gray as the ocean fog. His shoulders are broad and his arms quite muscular. He is wearing a sleeveless tunic of red-gold, with a wide multi-colored belt that picks up the colors of his tunic, and dark-hued pants. Like Demetra, his feet are scaled and his toes webbed. His scales appear to be almost the color of his hair, with a gold tint. Like their clothing, their scales seem to change in shimmering, rainbow colors.

Demetra begins, "Greetings, land-clinging Humans, from the Princess Demetra, daughter of Grania and Ordenon, Queen and King of Tesalafala Fields, which lie far beneath the ocean waves. There is a legend that when the moon rises high in the sky, you will see a moon also glimmering within the waters of the ocean. When far out at sea with no land in sight, the sailors of long ago would find comfort both in the image of the moon high above them and also in the moon shining up to them from beneath the waters. They referred to these two moons as the twin sisters of the moon. I know this legend is true for I have experienced it with my own eyes. Even when the moon in the sky is hidden behind the clouds, the moon in the water still shines, so that sailors far out at sea will never feel alone and can always count on the twin moons to light their way home. Therefore, we call the ocean Tesalafala Fields, the twin sisters of the moon.

"My mother and father have ruled their kingdom beneath the ocean for almost seven thousand years. It is a vast kingdom, much like your kingdoms in the physical Earth, with their great mountains and valleys and cities, though much smaller than those in the physical world. Like all the king-doms in Tír na nÓg, the larger city is usually the capitol, with much smaller villages scattered throughout the kingdom. My ancestors have always ruled this kingdom, but other sea kingdoms can be found much closer to our physical Mother Earth. In fact, in a not too distant past of your history, there still could be found Merpeople kingdoms in your physical realm. I think this you already know, since we are in many of your legends already. Even looking about Lili and Merlin's house, my people are featured in much of your artwork. I do have to admit there have been times when Merfolk (though not I personally, nor those of my family) have taken the role of sirens and lured ships full of men to the rocks, so that both they and their treasure sank far beneath the ocean waves. These sirens were usually from the darker realms, and such events happened long ago in days gone by. Most of our encounters with Human folk merely involved them glimpsing us as we sat upon the rocks, combing our hair or singing a song, which sometimes provided enticing entertainment for lonely seamen. We, especially the females of my people, are of a flirtatious nature.

"There have been times when we, like the Selkie people who are also our kin, have left the sea for a time and come upon the land and taken the form of a Human. Both females and males of our tribe have done this. The most usual reason is that we have fallen hopelessly in love with a Human being who lives next to the sea, or, in extremely rare cases, because we were banished there. Sometimes my people would take on Human form and live among the Humans for years, studying their ways, almost as spies, you might say. In these times of noisy machines, unpredictable Human behavior, and threats of war, we seldom now walk upon your land among Humans, at least in your physical realm. We do very often come in close contact with Humans who live in Tír na nÓg and, of course, with others of the Fair Folk.

Even to this day, we intermingle by marriage with Humans, Elves, Gnomes, and others. Since this may be the only chance I will have to speak with Humans who live in the physical realm, I would like to share some concerns with you.

"Mother Earth is your mother, and part of your mother is obviously the sea. All life was first born in the great sea of Creation, which is reflected in a much smaller scale on your physical Earth. Even in these days, life is still born in the great sea of Mother Earth. You were first born and later birthed from the sea within your mother's womb. The great sea upon which your ships now sail contains all the fish, dolphins, whales, and other sea creatures that live beneath your waves. There are even creatures there of which you may have no knowledge, such as the great Sea Dragons. I must make you understand that, as we watch Humanity pollute the great ocean of the Mother with garbage, oil, other pollutants, and nuclear waste, we feel a great rage against you and a great sense of incredulous disbelief. How can you be so foolish as to kill the ocean that gave you life and still brings you life to this day? The Mother's ocean sustains you. When you kill the ocean, you kill yourselves. Foolish, foolish, foolish Humans—you poison your air, you poison the water, and you poison the land. You are committing suicide. Do you not know it is against the teachings of the Holy Parents and our beloved brother, Jesus, to kill yourself, that all life is sacred? I think the day is coming that you will not drown in the ocean, but, instead, you will drown in your own filth.

"Do you find my words harsh? I speak them in the hope that perhaps they will make you angry, but at the same time help you to wake up. That is why (though you may think me an imaginary figment of folklore) I am more real than you are, because I do not think in a two-dimensional manner as you do. I am real. My beloved Mother Earth and her oceans are real. We Fair Folk are real. We are aware of all Creation that passes around us or through us. We are immersed in life, while you Humans are not. You are immersed in an illusionary world, and I tell you that you will become figures of folklore, not believed in. You and your kind will fade away if you do not wake up. Perhaps that is not exactly true. The Mother and Father love you, and, though my words may tear like a shark's teeth against your skin, I and my kind, Merpeople and others of the Fair Folk, do care about you and love you, as the Mother, Father, and Jesus love you. They will preserve many of you through the dark ages to come, but there will be far fewer Humans left upon the surface of the Mother, because, if your population continued to grow unchecked upon Mother Earth, eventually you would kill all Creation.

"My words are still coarse and angry, like a stormy sea. I do not wish to drown you beneath the waves of my wrath. Perhaps our next conversation will be more pleasant, and you will find me more charming. I plead with you, before you pollute something else, be it land, sea, or sky, at least stop and think what you are doing and take responsibility. Perhaps you will change and become a true child of the Mother and Father and Jesus, a true cousin or brother or sister to us of the Fair Folk, and a true child to Mother Earth. I will let Roth speak for a time now."

Roth continues, "It appears, after such hard words, it may be better for me to be the soft one, the gentle one, though I do agree with what my love says. She is, by nature, a very sweet, gentle woman, very nurturing to all creatures, even Humans, given the chance. I am just pointing this out to you, as you say, so that perhaps you may have a clearer understanding of my love. She is my heart, my sunlight beneath the waves. My task at this time is to touch briefly upon the various types of Fair Folk who are related to the Merpeople. In your physical world, we are related to all sea creatures, no matter what they may be. We are also related to the fish in your lakes and streams and to other animals who love the water, such as frogs, turtles, and even the ducks and swans. Any creature who loves the water is kin to us, including the Humans. Let me correct that statement. Humans are kin to us who love the water and do not add to its misery.

"What other creatures of folklore of our kind can I speak about? You have heard, of course, of the Water Nymphs. Though the majority of them prefer the clean, safe waters of Tír na nÓg, you can still find Water Nymphs, both male and female, in many lakes and streams even in your physical realm. If you are sensitive enough to spiritual matters, you will sense their presence in some particularly mystical lake or stream. These Water Nymphs prefer to wear no clothing, and both male and female are quite beautiful. Like us, they may come out of the water to sing haunting songs, which, on occasion, catch the fancy of a Human passing nearby. Contrary to legend, these songs are not always of a malevolent nature. In fact, the Humans who have heard our songs sometimes have become transformed for the better and gone on to be the great bards or teachers of your realm.

"Many times you will find Brownies next to the banks of the lakes and streams. Brownies are the little people, much smaller than Gnomes are, and they are quite friendly and enchanting. Though Brownies live everywhere, and you may find them in both mountains and valleys, one type of Brownie is known as the Water Brownie, and these dear, sweet little people would never travel very far from their home waters. Many of the Water Brownies do assist you Humans with the cleansing of your waters. It is not simply by machines your water is cleaned—it is also by these little helpers who bring you the sparkling water you drink.

"We wish to speak about one other group, and that is the Salmon people. Perhaps you have heard that the Salmon is a fish of great wisdom, and the longer they live and the more hazel nuts they consume, the wiser they become. Though quite rare in your realm, these Salmon people do exist, and they have the ability to shape-shift into the form of a Human. Though they may have a slight fish-like appearance, they can walk among Humans and dispense wisdom. I am not sure, but perhaps, if you look among the stories of the first people in your land, you will find stories about these Salmon people or of fish turning into people and back into fish. You may find reported in your legends that if you can catch one of these Salmon, roast it, and eat of its flesh, you will gain instant wisdom. Sadly, there may be some truth to this, but it would be much better if those who tasted the flesh of a Salmon had considered becoming their students instead. They would have learned far more from the very mouths of the Salmon people than from the eating of their flesh. On extremely rare occasions in the past, a fisherman caught yet another type of fish. This fish then offered the fisherman three wishes if he would free the fish and place him back into the water. Such fish are close kin of the Salmon people.

"I am not bringing these old stories back to your attention in order to inspire you to go out and try to catch one of these fish, for that is impossible in these modern times. Thanks to the Mother and Father, and to their own spiritual awareness, these beings cannot be caught in these times, but they can teach directly. Merlin has reminded me that spirit companion animals are discussed in another section of this book. The Salmon people would be the type of teachers to fall into this category.

"My lovely Demetra has suggested at this time that I may be putting our readers to sleep, so, if you have any further questions on this topic, perhaps you should seek out such companions yourself. I am glad for the time I was able to share with you to speak these words and bring these thoughts. I hope that our conversations have helped provide you with a clearer understanding of the Merpeople. Perhaps this will lead you to more insightful ways on how to live in harmony with all Creation, or at least to the awareness that others exist out there in Creation who are different from you. We do exist, and we have a great love for the Mother and Father Creator and for all Creation. We are a grand family awaiting your return to your rightful place among us. Keep continuing down your pathway of destruction, and you will be alone. Turn about and become again the children of the Mother Earth, and you will come home. Mother and Father's blessing upon you, and may the Mother's oceans bring you sustenance."

CHAPTER X

The Dragons

Another creature of folklore that thrives in the land of Tír na nÓg is the Dragon. At the time of this writing, my physical body is sitting in a comfortable chair in my home, but my spirit body is seated inside a vast cave. On one of the cave walls, cut through the thick stone, is a rounded opening that appears natural in shape. It allows a shaft of brilliant, white sunlight to pass through, forming a near circle on the floor of the cave. Within its brilliance, elements sparkle and dance. I am seated within that bright shaft of light upon a comfortable, wooden chair, nearly a throne, which is ornamented with beautiful woodcarvings. The chair is upholstered upon its seat and back with tapestry depicting a beautiful scene of nature. I seem to be the size of a small child sitting within this gigantic chair. Before me, within the same shaft of light and sitting quite comfortably directly on the floor of the cave, are four massive Dragons. They sit cross-legged in the Lotus posture, their great tails wrapped about them.

The heads of these Dragons are shaped like those of horses, with the strong jaws slightly wider, their mouths filled with many large, sharp, pointed teeth. Their necks are long and slender, though not unduly so, and they are very flexible. This flexibility allows them the ability to turn and look behind them as they fly. The males' shoulders are broad, while the females' are more slender. Their arms are long and muscular, shaped much like a Human arm. On each hand are six long fingers with long, sharp claws at the end. A seventh opposable thumb with a claw is located at the palm side of the hand near the wrist. When they choose to walk on all four limbs, this thumb functions as a dewclaw. While their bodies are slender, they are still muscular. The males' chests are broad, while the females' chests give a subdued impression of a Human female's body. Their body structure is, in many ways, comparable to that of a Human. Their stomachs are somewhat slender, and, at that point, the body begins to broaden out and become more muscular.

From behind, from out of their backbone and between their shoulder blades, sprout great, massive wings. These bat-shaped wings can unfold from their bodies like the wings of an eagle. They have the ability to fold these wings around their body like a cloak or to fold them back upon their backs, so that they almost appear to be rolled up against their body. The lower half of their bodies appears wider and more muscular, with strong legs and muscles to support their long, massive tails, which end (at least on these Dragons) with sharp, pointed tips that flatten out into a triangle. This triangle is very flexible, and, though it can remain soft in nature, it can harden suddenly to the sharpness of an axe's blade. Their legs are muscular, with the length comparable in structure to those of a Human. Their feet are wide and in the form of a rounded triangle shape, with the tip of the triangle at their heel. The wider part of the triangle spreads out into seven long toes, each of which ends in a very sharp claw. The bottom of each foot is covered in one long scale or horn, so that they suffer no discomfort from any surface upon which they may tread.

Three of the four Dragons are white, while one Dragon is of a deep red hue. The body of this red Dragon, who is known to us by the name of Mons, is entirely covered in scales. These scales fit so closely together that one can barely see the separation of one scale from another. Mons' eyes are slanted and the color of molten gold. Atop his head, growing close to his skull, appears a mane of thick, red hair, which grows longer as it flows from the back of his head down his long neck. Down to the shoulder blades and down his back, red fur grows as a close-cropped strip along his spine and tail.

Sitting next to Mons is Trill. Her body is completely covered in short, white fur. I am told that beneath this fur lie scales like those of Mons, though you would have to pull the fur back to find them. Her eyes, like Mons', are the color of molten gold and are even more slanted than his are. Her facial features, although she is a Dragon, are beautiful. Both Mons and Trill have sharp, pointy ears that rest close to their head. When relaxed, the tips of their ears bend slightly downward to cover the ear openings. When they become anxious or agitated, their ears point upwards sharply, harden, and give the appearance of horns upon their heads. Flowing outwards from Trill's head is a white mane, braided much like that of the hair of a young woman. Sparkling within her white braids are colored gemstones of reds and greens. Her mane flows thickly down her back, head, and shoulders. Like Mons, a strip of white hair travels along her spine and the tip of her tail. It appears the hair along her spine is longer than Mons' and covers the top part of her back, before becoming a narrow fur strip along her tail.

Sitting next to Trill is Grandmother Dragon, whose body, like Trill's, is covered in white fur. Though ancient, her body is still powerful and strong. Grandmother Dragon's mane is also quite long, with much thicker braids coursing down her back. Like Trill, a strip of fur travels along her spine and becomes smaller and narrower along her tail. Grandmother's slanted eyes are the color of blue ice; yet much warmth is to be found there. Finally, sitting next to her, is Grandfather Dragon, Grandmother's mate. His slanted eyes are also the color of blue ice, also with much warmth. The mane on top of his head is long and thickly braided, and he is gifted with a great, long, flowing white beard. His beard has been formed into many braids, which flow from his chin down to the middle of his stomach. His entire body is covered with hair, somewhat longer and shaggier than that of the others.

The Dragons before me are the size of four massive hills; yet they have made themselves appear somewhat smaller than normal for this occasion, since, in their true form, they are as tall as mountains. Before them, I am quite small, but I do not feel threatened. The walls of this cave, with its shaft of bright sunlight, rise far even above the Dragons' heads. So far up does the ceiling of this cave rise that it appears to me almost as high as the sky. The crystals growing from the ceiling sparkle like stars far above me.

Trill begins, "To the Human Tribe, greetings from the Dragon Tribe. I am Trill, wife and soul mate to Mons, the Dragon, and daughter to Cleeif and Orman, the Dragons otherwise known to those of my kind as Grand-mother and Grandfather Dragon. We join with you today in counsel, we, the beings of folklore, and you, the Humans of the physical world. We come to you as equals, and we hope and pray that your minds may throw off the hood of ignorance that limits your thoughts and, for this brief time, share with us the possibility of our existence. In ancient times, we dwelt on the physical Mother long before the coming of the Fair Folk and Humanity. We were among the first creatures that walked gently upon Mother Earth and flew among the clouds of her skies. You see, my new Human friends, we were not always the creatures of folklore that you believe us to be, for we did once exist on your physical Earth. In fact, even in these days, you have found many of our bones and display them in your museums. You know us by another name now, the creatures you refer to as Dinosaurs.

"At that time, there were many different types of Dragons, and many did not have wings as Dragons do today. There were the Land Dragons and Sea Dragons and Sky Dragons. In those far distant times, the Dragons lived peacefully on the Mother, sustained by the vegetation of the land. The first meat-eating Dinosaurs were born upon the fall of the Evil One (otherwise known as Lucifer) and after his impact upon Mother Earth, created out of the holocaust of his coming. You see, even in those times, the Dragons had consciousness and awareness of themselves and those around them, but the Evil One managed to deceive and distort many of them. Though the first Dragons were peaceful vegetarians and not carnivores, through the manipulation of the Evil One, the first meat-eating Dinosaurs were born, and they tragically fed upon their meeker cousins."

Mons continues, "The effect of the meat-eating Dinosaurs upon the vegetarian Dragons was terrible indeed, so terrible that the vegetarian Dragons had either to mutate into meat-eating Dinosaurs themselves in order to survive or develop other ways of protecting themselves. As your scientists have discovered among our bones, many Dragons developed horns or different types of body armor to combat the carnivorous Dinosaurs. There was a small population of Dragons, though, who went even farther in the development of ways to protect themselves. The direct ancestors of the Dragons today traveled together, either singly or in very small groups of two or three, into the most inhospitable areas of Mother Earth, into places where the meat-eating Dinosaurs would not dare to follow. They journeyed to places of extreme heat and fire, such as volcanic lands, or into areas of extreme cold, such as the lands of ice. It was within these extreme and inhospitable lands of fire and ice that the Fire Dragons and the Ice Dragons were first born. Some of the Dragons also traveled deep, deep beneath the ocean's waves, into the cold, dark regions of the ocean floors, where even the meat-eating sea Dinosaurs would not venture. This is where the Sea Dragons were born, for so deep did they travel that their bodies became hardened due to the pressure of the ocean depths and the coldness of the ocean deeps. They became invulnerable to the attacks of the less powerful ocean Dinosaurs, so that the predator became the prey of these great Sea Dragons.

"It was also at this time that the Land and Sea Dragons developed wings. The Land Dragons developed small winged appendages upon their backs, while the Sea Dragons' small wings were little more than fins. Within a few short millennia, however, these small wings and fins developed into great, massive wings, capable of lifting the bodies of the Sea and Land Dragons high above the clouds, where no meat-eating Dinosaur could travel. So great and powerful were their wings that they had the ability to create great hurricanes and other storms upon the surface of the Mother.

After a time, our direct ancestors, two of whom sit now before you in the forms of Grandmother and Grandfather, were able to attack these meat-eating Dinosaurs from sea and land and sky with breath of fire and ice and mighty storms of wind from their great wings. Their teeth and claws became much larger, as did their tails, developing into whip-like weapons that could be used to slash and tear into the meat-eating Dinosaurs.

"So terrible was the Dragons' effect upon them that I daresay the meat-eating Dinosaurs would have been the first Dinosaurs to become extinct, were it not for the great change brought by the Mother and Father in the form of a giant planet which passed close to the surface of the Earth. In learning to defend ourselves, our mental ability increased to the extent that we learned even to travel into other realms that lay next to Mother Earth. In some ways, the meat-eating Dinosaurs should be thanked. It was because of them that we developed the ability to protect ourselves and travel into these safer realms. There we escaped the horrific Armageddon-type holocaust that rained down upon the others of our kin, both the peaceful and meat-eating Dinosaurs alike. The devastation caused by the planet resulted in their virtual extinction or, as your scientists say, the end of the Dinosaur age. It was shortly after the passing of the errant planet that the people of the Fair Folk and Humans appeared upon the Earth, created in the image of the Mother and Father Creator. There were still, even at that time, some Dinosaurs existing who had survived the passing of the planet, but their age was swiftly coming to an end. It was at this point where your scientists could draw the distinction between Dinosaurs and Dragons, for while Dinosaurs became extinct, Dragons did not.

"At that time, the end of the Dinosaur age, Mother Earth had become a beautiful garden, and we, the Dragons, lived in harmony with the Human and Fair Folk tribes, as did all of the other animals and beings of Creation. Sadly, after the Humans' separation from their Fair Folk brothers and sisters and through the millennia, Humans began to see their Dragon kin as threats. Therefore, not only did the Humans wage war upon their Fair Folk family, but they also waged war against the Dragons.

"It is true some Dragons, in their rage against the Humans, were again twisted and manipulated by the Evil One and adopted the ways of the meat-eating Dinosaurs before them. These are the ones who became the true threat to Humanity. The single goal of the carnivorous Dragon mind was the extinction of all Humans, and even Fair Folk, upon the planet. These are the symbolic representations of the evil Dragons or serpents in the Bible, especially in the Book of Revelation. These terrible creatures still exist in the dark realms. In contrast, though, many Dragons live within the realms close to your physical realm and beyond, and they love the Mother, Father, and Jesus and wish no harm to the Fair Folk, Humanity, or any of the Mother's children. We who are conversing with you today belong to that tribe of Dragons."

Grandmother Dragon continues, "Over the years, the Dragons who served the Mother and Father were given special tasks. The Land Dragons, and I do call them Land Dragons, even though they have great wings upon their back, were given the task of protecting Mother Earth, the physical land itself. These Land Dragons, in spirit, lay beneath and within the earth of the Mother. They lie peacefully asleep, unless the Mother and Father bid them awaken to defend the land and the people who live upon the land, or, sadly, to correct the people of the land, or to change the terrain of the land, which takes place through great earthquakes or volcanic eruptions.

"The Dragons of the ocean may help calm the sea, so that sailors can arrive safely at their destinations, or, again, upon the duty given to them by the Mother and Father, may cause great, raging storms which wreak havoc upon the land, sometimes in the form of great waves. There have been times when the Sea Dragons have actually covered entire nations with great waves. The Dragons of the air can cause clouds to form and rain to fall. With the power of their massive wings, they can cause great storms to descend upon the Earth.

"Understand we are given different tasks by the Mother and Father. Some we enjoy performing; others we do not. We do not wish harm upon Mother Earth or any of her children, but we may be given a task to perform, so that a change will come. We must bring about these changes, sometimes by violent means, at the will of the Mother and Father. Though we are from three spheres of influence—earth, sea, and sky, we are divided into four main tribes—the elemental Dragons of earth, air, fire, and water. Our duties often overlap one another, and, because of this overlap in our way of life, there is no true separation of these groups between us. I only give the separation of the four tribes, though they are loosely held, so that you may have some understanding of us."

Grandfather Dragon continues here, "In these last words of our discussion, I will try to clarify our purpose in your modern times. In the coming years, Dragons will once again be found within Human consciousness. We will no longer be creatures of folklore, for you will be able to find us within the physical world. We Dragons will once again be found upon the physical Mother, upon the land, in your skies, and in your seas. Sadly, there will be many of the dark Dragons, who will cause great destruction to Mother Earth and to Humanity. These dark Dragons will, of course, be servants of the Evil One. Thankfully, though, you will also discover the Dragons of the Mother and Father Creator and their beloved son, Jesus, whose task will be to protect Humanity and protect Mother Earth to the best of their abilities. It is my deepest wish, within my heart's Grail cup, that you will focus upon us, the Dragons who serve the Mother and Father and Jesus, so that, upon our arrival on the physical Mother, you will wish to enlist our aid in the fight against evil. It is our wish, as well, that we, the Dragons, and others of the Fair Folk and Humanity and all of Creation will once again become one large family. I, Grandfather Dragon, and the other three Dragons present here before Merlin and you who read these words, ask the Holy Family to send their blessing upon you and pray that some day we will meet again as friends and family.

The Trolls

Here follows the story of Grief, the Troll, his experiences as a Troll, and his insights concerning the dark Faerie. Grief's physical body structure is that of a very large, muscular giant. Though at present he appears smaller in order to fit comfortably within our home, the typical height of a Troll is twelve to fifteen feet tall, with males being closer to fifteen feet in height, while females are closer to the twelve-foot mark. Grief sits, at this moment, in a rocking chair in our library. He is dressed in rust-colored trousers and a rust-colored tunic. Over his tunic, he wears a smaller, dark brown vest, with bronze studs on the shoulders and down the front of both sides of his chest. Large, heavy, dark brown boots that come up to his knees cover his feet. What flesh I can see is covered with a light brown or blondish fur that lies close to the skin. His hands are huge, much like Human hands, with four fingers and an opposable thumb. His fingernails are thicker, longer, and more sharply pointed than Human nails, but not so long as to impede his ability to use his fingers or hands properly to grasp or hold an object.

His large face is in proportion to his body, and his facial structure gives the impression of looking directly into the face of a lion, with the lion's mane beginning low on his forehead and growing back over his head and traveling down to his shoulders and beyond. His mane, or hair, is of a darker, richer brown, with blondish streaks the color of his skin. It is braided into thick braids, almost like dreadlocks, as is his great beard, which is thick and braided and flows down to the middle of his stomach. His nose, in appearance, is similar to a nose you would find upon a lion's face, wide and close to the face. The nostrils are large and would flare if he were to become provoked. His eyes are large and slanted upwards with the typical Faerie tilt.

What are quite noticeable in his facial structure are his strong, powerful jaws, which show the upper and lower canine teeth. All his teeth grow into points, but his front teeth are much longer. Even with his mouth closed, they are quite prominent, especially when he smiles. The teeth almost give the impression of a young boar's tusks protruding from his mouth. Growing out of his mane at the top of his forehead are great horns like those of a ram. Grief tells me that, once these horns are grown, Trolls do not lose them, but carry them throughout adulthood. He says the women of his people also grow horns upon their heads, though they are not as large as the horns of the males. They have great manes of hair like the males, but without the beard, and they have a light covering of hair growing closely upon all their exposed skin. The women also have incisors, not quite as large as the males, though the females' teeth, like the males, are all pointed.

Grief begins his story. "I am one of the reborn Trolls, one of the civilized Trolls who live in Tír na nÓg, the land next to the Mother and Father Creator. Many of my kind, however, are not civilized Trolls, but are of the Babasi clan. Babasi, a word from the Troll tongue, describes most of the Trolls who exist as the enslaved spirits, the enslaved ones or the dark Trolls. Unlike the free Trolls, they wear hardly any clothing. Most of their clothing is made of animal skins, the skins of their victims, or the skins of poor souls killed in battle, be it Troll skins, or, many times, Human skins, Fair Folk skins, or Hobgoblin skins. A Troll of the dark side would never put boots on his feet. Our feet are large and hairy with long claws, or toenails, if you will. Trolls in the dark realms just wrap their feet in skins or fur and lace it together with cord. Their clothing is not as sophisticated as what we wear in the light realms. Over many millennia, we, the Trolls of Light of Tír na nÓg, have copied the clothing styles of our neighbors around us in Tír na nÓg. We find ourselves very comfortable in such styles, which now feel quite natural to us.

"Let me first speak about my brothers and sisters in the dark realms, for, even though we have met and will meet again upon the battlefield and try to kill one another, I still have compassion for them in my heart. They are manipulated by the Evil One, and their tortured spirits know only pain and suffering. Because of this, they give pain and suffering to others around them, many times even to members of their own families, be it their wives or their children, whoever is within striking distance of their wrath. Killing others, in some way, momentarily eases the suffering of their own spirits. It is as if, through murder, the terrible weight upon their souls is lifted ever so slightly, but that is only an illusion given to them by their evil master. This is the typical life of a Troll in the dark realm.

"We are born to suffering, and, as children, we spend most of our days and nights trying to stay alive. Many Trolls do not survive even into what you would call early childhood; they do not live long enough to become toddlers. Seldom are they killed by their mother, but usually by their father, who kills the child out of anger or for food. Sometimes the children are killed by others of their community or, many times, a child will meet his or her death from the animals found in the dark realms. When a child is able to walk or, better yet, to run, the child will flee to the heavy forests, away from the Troll settlements, to take their chances with the monsters of the dark forest. This is where they learn their survival skills, and the ones who actually reach adulthood in these dark forests are very strong and almost impossible to kill. For a child to grow to the point where he can run and somewhat fend for himself is a gift given to him by his mother. Though it is hard to believe it of such a savage life, a Troll mother is quite defensive of her children and will fight to the death to protect her child. Even though the child may, as an adult, later take her life, within a mother Troll's heart lies the need to protect her young and see them at least grow to the point where they can fend for themselves in the dark forest and, hopefully, mature to become adults.

"The homes or huts in the dark realms of the Trolls are made of thick branches bent to form a dome over which animal skins and the skins of those killed in battle are spread. In some ways, these rounded huts resemble a nightmarish version of a Gnome's home. In front of these homes, you will always find the skulls of those killed in battle or various other beings roasting over a fire, some Troll, but some more Human in nature, and some other terrible animals that you Humans would never consider eating. Let me make a point here that Humans are closely related to the light Elves in Tír na nÓg and the dark Elves in the dark realms, but they are almost as closely related to the Trolls in the dark realms and, of course, to the Trolls in the light realms. Humanity actually has more in common with the Trolls of the dark realms than with those of the light realms, due to your mannerisms, the food you eat, and the way you make war and its after-effects.

"Not only are the Trolls of the dark realms savaged by their own kind and by other creatures of the dark forest, but they are also savaged by the Evil One's dark fallen angels, who torment them with their rods of lightning, which scorch their skins and cause them to have convulsions upon the ground. These fallen angels are quite beautiful to look upon, and, though their nature is pure evil, in appearance they resemble the Fair Folk of the light realms of Tír na nÓg, which causes those of the dark realms to hate the Fair Folk of the light realms even more.

"A Troll must also contend with parasites in the forms of different types of worms, which eat their intestines and sometimes bore through the outer layer of their skin. These worms can sometimes be the size of a large snake in your realms, but they can also be smaller. A nest of them can erupt outward from the skin from the inside, thereby driving the Trolls into tormented rages. The ticks, another form of large parasite, fasten themselves to one's skin and hang there as great bags of blood. Other horrible insects include giant spiders, sometimes larger than the Trolls themselves, which form great webs to capture an unsuspecting Troll or other creature. The spider will wrap them in the web, and, over time, make of the Troll or the captured being a spider's meal by slowly draining away their vital juices. Other spiders do not create webs, but, instead, run faster than your horses (and they are about the same size, in fact). They run down their prey and leap upon them, inserting their long, poisonous fangs into the back of the victim's neck, turning their victim into a long, slow, painful meal. I could go on and on, for whatever menaces you in the physical realm, whether it be mosquitoes, ants, or snakes, were you to enlarge them several times and make them as terrifying as possible, you would find them in the dark realm, for it is a place of nightmares.

"My own experience must be told. I was born in the dark realms. Like all Troll mothers, my mother fiercely defended me. One day, just at the time when I could run and begin to take some care of myself, my mother was killed while defending me from my father and my older brother. I saw them kill her with my own eyes, but I was too small to do anything about it, so I fled into the dark woods. Finally, after many years of painful suffering, I grew into adulthood and returned to my father's hut. By this time, he had taken another female to be his mate, and I killed him with my own war club.

I would not cut out his heart and his brain and eat them, as is a Troll custom, for doing so would have given my father honor. Instead, I dragged his body to the dark forest and let the spiders and other creatures from that dark wood feast upon him, thereby dishonoring him. My brother, enraged by the death of our father and, even more so, by my dishonoring of our father, met me in battle, and I killed him. His body I buried, a most unTroll-like thing to do.

"I met a woman. Her name is Tears. I fell in love with her in a very unTroll-like manner, cared for her deeply, and treated her quite well. Never did I strike her or even threaten to strike her. Whatever food I found in the dark realms, I shared equally with her, and perhaps I gave her even more than her share. She, in many ways, was also very unTroll-like. Our hut was very clean and consisted of animal skins only, with no skins from our victims. Outside our hut, there were only a few skulls of those I had killed in battle. We did not try to murder others in our community, and we were openly loving with one another. Because of my father's position in our tribe as a chieftain and due to my inheritance of that role through the murder of my father and brother, I became chieftain. You see, to be a murderer in the dark realms is to be held in high esteem.

"I have not lived a saintly life, for I fought beside other Trolls in the battlefield against the Fair Folk of light, and I have taken some of their lives, thereby cutting short their immortality. In one battle, an Elven warrior wounded me grievously, but he did not end my immortal life. Instead, in a quite unElven-like manner, he spared my life and even treated my wounds, so that I survived. No other of my Troll neighbors knew what had happened, but I knew, and, at first, I felt confusion and shame that he had spared my life and not taken it as was proper. I believed, at first, that he thought my head unworthy to adorn the front of his hut and had thereby spared my life, not out of compassion, but out of revulsion. Yet, I thought to myself, that could not be right, for he did clean and bind my wounds and even bring me near to my own hut outside my village, so I could return home to my wife, my beloved Tears. She cared for my wounds from that point until I grew strong enough to stand upon my own, which, as a Troll, you must learn to do quickly or be killed by the others. No sign of weakness is tolerated among the dark Trolls.

"Upon regaining my strength, I would visit the extreme borders of the dark realms which lay against the realms of light. These invisible borders would burn a being such as me at the very touch. After a time, to test my strength against these walls of golden light, I would push my hands against them, and my hands would begin to burn and smoke. Then I pushed my body against these barriers, and my body began to burn and my fur began to smoke. I wasn't sure why I continued to do so, but a sense of urgency began to fill me. My beloved Tears was pregnant with our son, and I realized, at one point, that I did not wish him to be born in the dark realms, but to be born in the realms of light.

"Spiritually-corrupted by the Evil One, I stood with my body pressed up against this golden barrier, feeling my dark, tormented spirit and body burn against the barrier of the light realm. Unimaginable pain flared through my entire being; yet I continued to press forward. Then I noticed, on the other side of the golden barrier, an Elf stood watching me, and he began to encourage me and call to me and reach for me. It amazed me. Why would this Elf full of light want to help a being such as me? This Elf, whose name I later would learn was Emrys, literally reached his hands into the dark realm and grasped my now smoldering hands. With him pulling and me pushing, he dragged me through that golden barrier. So terrible was my pain as I crossed the barrier that I thought my entire being had burst into an all-consuming flame, and that there would be nothing left of me but ash. I thought this was to be the death of me, for how could a dark-filled being such as I enter the realms of light?

"What had been taken from me in the flame was the clothing I had worn made of animal skins and, thankfully, also, the great tick parasites that clung to my body. They fell from my body and lay screeching like tortured swine around me as the fire consumed them. I had survived, but my immediate concern was for my wife and my future son, for, without me to protect them, she and my unborn son would quickly be killed or taken by another Troll. Even more amazing to me was that other Elves and Gnomes and Sprites came and bound my wounds, put ointments upon the burns on my body, and gave me food to eat and liquid to drink which helped heal my body. The further transformation of my soul, however, would only come with diligent hard work on my part, and it took several years for my transformation to be completed.

"I fell asleep for a time from exhaustion. When I awoke, I found myself lying upon a soft bed filled with herbs, my head cradled by a female Elf, while a male Gnome gave me more liquid to drink. I immediately expressed my angst about my beloved Tears and our unborn son. To my profound gratitude, they were able to summon my wife by linking with my mind and using the ability to communicate telepathically with her. It is hard for me to speak this part. Great joy filled my heart for she actually came to the golden barrier. She did not have to do that. She could have stayed where she was and taken up with another male Troll, but she came to the barrier.

"We had talked about crossing the barrier into the light realms before, but it was merely talk, more of a frightening dream that we did not seriously consider. Still, she saw me in the realms of light of Tír na nÓg and heard my pleadings for her to join me, so that she and our son would be safe. Combined with this was my threat that, if she did not come to the realms of light, I would return to her in the dark realms, so that I could protect her and the child and live the best life we could in such a terrible place. I know it was because of her love for me and her fear that I would give up what I had gained through so much pain—that I would give it all up for the love of her and our unborn child—and because of her love for the child within her womb, that she, too, crossed the golden barrier. She was actually pulled directly through the golden barrier by the Elves and Gnomes present. I am happy to say that she did not suffer as badly as I did, although it was not a pleasant experience for her.

"Over the millennia, many of the dark Trolls have turned their backs on their evil ways and crossed into Tír na nÓg, even though they suffer great pain in doing so. Though we, now the Trolls of Light, have fought alongside our Elven and Gnome brothers and sisters on the field of battle against the Trolls and other dark beings of the dark realms, we still have great compassion for the ones we leave behind. Unceasingly, we pray for those in the dark realms, and, through the Mother and Father and Jesus' love, I have finally found the ability to forgive my father, forgive my brother, and forgive those who brought me so much suffering there. Every day you will find us standing just beyond the golden barrier in Tír na nÓg, calling to our Troll brothers and sisters in the dark realms to come join us, pleading with them, reaching out for them. This we will continue to do until the return of our brother Jesus.

"Let me clarify that the Trolls of the light realms can enter the dark realms and have done so in times of battle. We can now easily cross back into the light realms and suffer no pain, for our spirits have changed, as have our bodies. The reason we stand within the realms of light, the realm of Tír na nÓg, and call to those who dwell in the dark lands is because those Trolls and other beings must, by their own will, give up their dark ways and be reborn by crossing that barrier on their own. They must at least attempt to cross the barrier on their own, for, by the very act of trying, we can pull them through. Merlin has asked me to clarify when the transformation of the heart or spirit comes—is it in the dark realms or when they reach the realm of Tír na nÓg? It is when they hear the Mother and Father and Jesus' voice calling to them, which is in the dark realms. When they hear that call and respond to it, that is when the transformation begins, and that is when they cross into the realms of light.

"Now, to give you a better picture of the dark realms, I will describe some of the other beings who dwell there. Among these beings are dark dragons, reptilian monsters, and vicious dragon snakes that crawl along the ground, hang high above in the trees, or swim in the dark ponds of that realm. Different types of terrible insects and other furry beasts and carnivores feed on anything they can kill, whether it be their own kind or other creatures. Great birds you would call shrikes swoop down from the skies and take their prey, even Trolls many times.

"Certain beings in the dark realms bear a resemblance to the Fair Folk from the realms of light, part Humanoid and part animal; yet their combination in the dark realms is more of a nightmare, and no beauty dwells within their forms. There are dark, small beings there that, in some ways, resemble Brownies, but they are actually nothing like them. They have sharp teeth and wander in large packs, leaping upon their unsuspecting prey and biting them to death. Interestingly enough, no Sprite-like beings exist in those realms. There are beings there who are about the size of Gnomes, perhaps a bit larger—more of the stature of a small man—and they are referred to as Hobgoblins. They are very hairy, with twisted features you would find unpleasant to look upon. They wear clothing that, in some ways, is quite fine; you would find it pleasant to look upon, even though it is in combination with animal skins. These Hobgoblins do use swords, clubs, axes, and shields. They wear armor and are one of the more intelligent tribes of the dark realms. Of course, you also have the dark Elves, who are very beautiful to look upon; yet their features give a feeling of unpleasantness and unhealthiness, like a fallen angel.

"Goblins stand ten to twelve feet tall, both men and women. The men have no hair, eyelashes, or eyebrows, and their skin is of a sickly, pale color with a greenish tint. Their bodies are fleshy, yet muscular, and they are just as strong as the Trolls are. The Trolls and Goblins have a very terrible odor about them, so strong that you can smell them from quite a distance away. It is hard for a Troll or Goblin to take their victims by stealth, because of their smell, and usually they do not bother anyway. If they wish to creep up on a victim, they must do it downwind. In contrast, the Hobgoblins and dark Faerie do not have a strong scent, although you might notice a sweet, perfumed, decaying smell.

"The Goblin males are about twelve to thirteen feet tall. They carry great clubs, war axes, and shields, and, like the Trolls, they wear less armor than the Hobgoblins or the dark Faerie do. Some of the Goblins will wear a helm to protect their great bald heads, but a Troll will not even consider wearing a helm, for it is considered an act of weakness. Our skulls are thicker than any helm ever created anyway. The female Goblins have a bit more hair, though it is thin, and they wear it in braids upon their head. They have eyelashes and eyebrows, and usually their hair varies from blue to green. Some have red hair and are very highly sought after. Otherwise, like their male counterparts, they are hairless on the rest of their body. A female Goblin, like a female Troll, is definitely female in shape.

"It is the Trolls, the dark Elves, the Hobgoblins, and even the dark Brownies who are the most aware of the races of the dark realms. The Goblins tend to be slow-witted. The female Goblin mothers, like the female Troll mothers, protect their young fiercely. The dark Elves and Hobgoblins, whether they be male or female, do not treat their children as severely as do the Troll and Goblin males. Ogres are the offspring of Goblins and Trolls and take on the characteristics of either the father or the mother. They can be hairy or bald. Most of them tend to have bluish or greenish skin or grey skin. They can be very clever or very dimwitted. In height, they are closer to Trolls, but in actions, they are less trustworthy than Hobgoblins and Trolls and crueler. Ogres cannot have offspring.

"I, as a free Troll who was once part of the dark realms, by observing your physical realm here, see many in Humanity who act much like the Fair Folk of the dark realms, which I find quite surprising. Because of these Humans willing to dwell with so much darkness in their lives, the spiritual veil that separates your physical realm from the dark realms is becoming very thin and porous. In the future, unless Humanity turns around, you, as a people, will come face to face with your close kin of the dark realms, be they Troll, dark Elf, Hobgoblin, or Goblin. Therefore, as I plead with my brothers and sisters in the dark realms, now I plead with Humanity, turn around your lives. Turn to the Mother and Father and Jesus. It was not I who changed me, and it was not Emrys who changed me. It was the love of the Mother and Father and Jesus.

"Walk gently upon Mother Earth, and let the love of the Mother and Father and Jesus fill you and turn your darkening physical realm into a realm of golden light like Tír na nÓg. I, Grief, a free Troll of Tír na nÓg, ask the Mother and Father's blessing and the blessing of Jesus and of our beloved Mother Earth upon you all, that from my tale understanding may come."

CHAPTER XI

The King of the Polar Bears

The information that follows comes from one of our power animals. We use the term "power animal" for the benefit of readers who may have explored some of the existing shamanic literature. To be quite honest, we are not particularly happy with the term "power animal." We prefer instead the terms "spirit companion" or "animal companion," and we will use these terms interchangeably through the rest of this section. Our guest is Bear, who, as his name suggests, is a bear—a massive, white bear of the Polar Regions. Like other spirit companions, he has the ability to change his size to better fit his environment, and so he has reduced his vast size enough to enter our home. He can barely fit in the room, even sitting directly on the floor.

Bear begins, "Merlin has asked me to come and speak with you concerning the matter of spirit companions or animal companions. Some of you reading this may have dabbled in a shamanic culture that frequently joins in partnership with an animal companion, while other readers will have no knowledge of such matters. Animal companions, spirit companions, or, if you prefer, power animals have been in partnership with those pilgrims, those questers of the spirit world, since time began. Long ago, when we were all one people, spoke one tongue, and dwelt in the same realm, it was quite normal for a Human to go directly to an animal and ask for assistance and guidance. The animal, if willing to become a spiritual mentor to the Human, would verbally communicate to the seeker in the same language. Sadly, it is difficult for Humans to experience this same type of partnership and communication between animal and Human in these modern times of this physical realm. In fact, I believe I can quite safely say that most Humans, and perhaps even those of you reading this chapter, see animals as dumb creatures, spiritually and intellectually inferior to Humanity.

"Sadly, in this realm, most of the animals Humans encounter appear to have lost the power of speech and, seemingly, the power of higher intellect. This is how it appears to Humanity, at least, although this may not actually be true. An idea I would like to place in your head, from a great, big, dumb Polar Bear, is that your world and how you view it is more illusionary than you think. Your reality is made up of dim shapes in the fog. In full sunlight, they fade away to nothingness. It is doubtful, however, that you would believe it possible to have a spiritually stimulating conversation with your dog or cat or with an animal you meet in your neighborhood or in the wild, so let us focus instead on the animal spirit companions who dwell within the spirit lands.

"I, Bear, am one of these spirit companions. I spend much of my time counseling Lili and Merlin from the realm of spirit, the kingdom of Tír na nÓg. There I can be with my family, safe and cozy, and I do not need to endure the difficulties I would encounter in the physical world (though I have crossed into your physical world in the past and will continue to do so in the present and the future). In my opinion, it is most beneficial for a Human, when given the opportunity, to work with an animal spirit companion. Not only will the Human's spiritual conceptions and awareness be broadened, but the companion animal will also gain and grow spiritually from his or her encounters with a Human ally. Though the Human will take the role of student, and the animal companion will accept the role of mentor or teacher throughout the process of this relationship, both Human and animal will learn from one another and prosper in their spiritual quests.

"Humans who seek out a companion animal should be quite sincere and should be open-minded enough to accept with respect whatever animal wishes to help them, whatever animal develops a desire to help them, and whatever animal is sent to them by the Mother and Father. There have been many encounters between Humans and their companion animals where the Human expected to be approached by what is considered a noble animal, such as an Eagle or a Stag or a Horse or even the mighty Bear; instead, a Mouse or a wee Bird or a tiny Frog approached the Human. Understand that Spirit knows what animal is best for you. Perhaps the companion animal you encountered was also expecting someone completely different, but got you instead. My advice when it comes to spirit companion animals is not to be a snob. A mentor who is a spirit Mouse can be as great a teacher as the largest Bear.

"I am sure some of you have read in books how best to encounter us and how to forge a relationship with us. What I am about to tell you may or may not agree with your previous studies. Understand that we seek you out before you seek us. Spirit animals are constantly seeking out Humans with whom to converse and share wisdom. Sadly, most of the Human population never hear their voices and never encounter them, even though they may be standing in front of them in spirit and even physically. Those of you who wish to have a spirit animal for a mentor, take heart. You have already gone quite a distance on the pathway to a successful encounter.

"You can meet an animal spirit companion in more than one way. You can go to someone who has skills as a shaman, or to a priest or priestess or elder, and they will help you connect with your animal spirit companion. This method of encountering animal spirit companions has been used with much success since before the written history of Humanity. These are modern times, however, and, though I may risk angering some of them as I say this, not all modern shamans are of the same caliber as their predecessors. Therefore, carefully select the person you wish to help you cross the bridge into the spiritual worlds to meet your animal spirit companions. Let me make a bold statement here and say that I, as an animal spirit companion, feel that it would be better for most Humans to make contact with their animal spirit companion on their own. Let us put aside here any worries that perhaps you will select the wrong animal or the wrong animal will select you, perhaps you are imagining the whole thing, or perhaps you will get an animal you do not want, and so on and so on. Put all these fears into a box, and bury it in the ground somewhere deep in Mother Earth. Let me try to provide you with steps, so that your encounter with your spirit animal companion may be easily accomplished.

"Step 1—Ask the Mother and Father for help in finding your animal companions.

"Step 2—Notice what animals you have encounters with in the physical world, be these animals inside your home or outside your home, or even animals you see in your magazines or on your television. What animal keeps appearing before you?

"Step 3—Watch your dreams, the ones when you are asleep and the ones when you are wide awake, otherwise referred to as daydreams.

"Step 4—Take a meditative journey, best accomplished by lying flat on your back in your bed during the daylight hours when you do not normally sleep. With calm, restful, deep breathing, allow yourself, within your mind, to enter a natural environment pleasing to you. I wish to make clear to you that whether your pleasing environment be a beach or a forest or a desert, the animal that is willing to work with you may not belong to those environments naturally. Do not fret. If a great, big Polar Bear appears before you in a scorching desert, it is because the meeting was meant to take place, no matter what the environment. Should it appear that the meeting between the two of you is going well, and there is a potential for a partnership, then, just as you would with any new-found friend, get to know them better.

"Make yourself comfortable, and sit down and have a chat with them in the spirit realm. Interview them; ask them questions about how they can help you spiritually and what they need from you, so that a relationship may be formed. You should find that most willing animal spirit companions will require no more of you than sincerity and a desire and a commitment to grow spiritually. There should be no strange talk of you committing any unusual acts to keep them beside you. If they ask you to do something that makes you feel uncomfortable with the request, then decline and move on. You will find the correct spirit animal companion in time. It may be the same kind of animal you encountered before or a completely different animal, but understand that you must feel comfortable with your animal companion, and they must feel comfortable with you. It is the same when you are meeting a stranger and begin a conversation with her. For a friendship to develop, there must be some mutual interest between the two of you. If not, a friendship will not develop, is this not true? Look at it in the same way when forming a relationship with an animal spirit companion. Once you have found the right spirit companion, and she has found you, then you can begin your relationship as student and teacher and, even more importantly, as true friends.

"Step 5—When you return to the physical world, do everything you can to learn more about how your animal companion lives in the physical world. How do your spirit animal's physical cousins in this realm live? How do they behave? Where do they live? What food do they eat? In other words, learn all you can about them, for you will find as you deal with your spirit companion that, though they have great spiritual awareness and the power of speech, they also will possess many of the same traits as their cousins in the physical realm.

"Step 6—Journey to them often. Set aside, if possible, the same time every day or every week to meet with them. Keep a notebook beside your bed when you journey, in order that, upon returning to the physical world, you can write down notes, so you do not forget anything you have learned from your animal spirit companion.

"Step 7—Let your relationship with them grow. Let it be one of mutual respect. Open your journal often to read of your journeys with them, and see and allow yourself to witness the change within your spirit and even the change outside of yourself. Through your experiences with your spirit animal companion, learn to walk more gently upon Mother Earth and have respect for all beings in Creation and respect for your Mother and Father Creator. If your animal companion is teaching you correctly, this last step will not be a step you need to think about, for it will come to you naturally. You will make this step without thought on your part, and you will truly be a changed Human being.

"Seven steps—hopefully they are not too many steps for you to accomplish. Hopefully, you will not become tired of climbing them or walking down them, whichever direction you choose to journey in.

"Let me add one last word here on a subject which Merlin has brought to my attention. A tradition is held in certain shamanic teachings that, once you meet your animal spirit companion or power animal, you must dance with them or dance for them, so that they will stay by your side. Let me say that, yes, we animal companions do love to dance, by ourselves or with our family, and we will even dance with you if you wish. However, to be honest, I and any other companion animal I have ever known (and over my long, long life, I have met many) do not require this. I think that an animal companion would perhaps wander off if they were bored due to your inattention. This would not happen, however, because you did not dance with them or perform some strange ritual for them. Any friendship, no matter how sincere or deep, can fade away if one or both parties do not pay attention to one another. Yet I would also like to point out that we spirit animal companions are capable of an astounding amount of loyalty to our Human students. Even though we may be ignored for an amount of time in your physical life, you may still find us waiting for you in the spirit world at the end of your life, ready to help you continue with your spiritual studies. When it comes to Human emotions and feelings, ours run, in my opinion, much deeper and truer and not so shallow. In closing, let me say that we will make a commitment to you that will last a lifetime, but please show us the consideration of being willing to make that commitment to us in return.

"Mother and Father's Blessings upon you and best of luck to you in your search for an animal companion. May you be a blessing to one another, may you learn from one another, and may you each become teachers to one another."

Professor Woodrow Woodchuck

Our next guest is well qualified to provide his own introduction, as clearly evidenced by his chosen profession.

"Please allow me to introduce myself. I am Professor Woodrow Woodchuck. My appearance is that of a common Woodchuck or Groundhog, such as you might find in your yard, the forest, or even wandering along the roadside. Yet, I think, if you were to see me during your travels outdoors, you would notice my uniqueness in comparison to the Woodchucks of the Human realm. You see, I tend to exhibit a fascination with clothing, such as trousers, dress shirts, vests, and jackets. However, I hold no appreciation for shoes. I prefer my lower feet to be unclad, so that I may feel the touch of my Mother Earth upon the pads of my feet.

"Into my vest pocket is neatly tucked an old pocket watch given to me by my great, great, great grandfather (who is still alive, by the way). The lifespan of animals in Tír na nÓg is much vaster than the lifespan of animals in your realm or even of Humans. During my long life, many generations of Humans have come and gone, from the cradle to the grave and their bones turned to dust, while I still survive in the kingdom of Tír na nÓg. Though my eyesight is keen and quite sharp, out of vanity, I wear small half spectacles on the bridge of my nose (what small bridge there is). I do on occasion wear a hat, usually a top hat, sometimes a derby, but generally, I prefer to stroll about with my head uncovered. In habit, I am quite British, for I do prefer my tea during the appropriate tea times, morning, afternoon, and, of course, evening. I do also enjoy indulging, on occasion, in a small glass of an intoxicant, usually brandy.

"Finally, not to bore you further with descriptions of myself or my attire, let me briefly inform you that I am a professor at one of the many universities in Tír na nÓg. I would share the name of the university with you, but it is in the high tongue of the Fair Folk and is nearly unpronounceable in Human speech. I have been a tenured professor at this particular university for over a millennium. My field of study is that of political science and sociology. My interest in these studies, of course, covers the kingdoms of Tír na nÓg and the light realms closer to the Mother and Father and our beloved brother, Jesus, but also the realms closer to the physical Mother Earth and even the darker realms beyond her. To put it more plainly, my studies not only involve the realm of the Faerie, but also the realm of the

Humans. When I refer to the dark realms, I refer to the Trolls, Goblins, Hobgoblins, and other dark creatures and monsters it might be better for you not to become acquainted with. Now, enough introduction of myself; let me, if I may, begin my lecture in the brief space I have within these pages.

"Perhaps you have become aware of the differences between the animal kingdom in your realm in comparison to the animal kingdom of Tír na nÓg and the realms closer to the Mother and Father. We animals in the kingdoms closer to the Mother and Father seem to have more cognitive abilities. At least it appears thus to you in the illusionary realm of the Humans. I would like to invite you, however, to become open to the awareness that the animals in your realm also have cognitive abilities that you may find quite remarkable. Perhaps these cognitive abilities are expressed most clearly in the form of their instincts and their ability to survive in a sometimes-harsh environment. I am sure you are aware, within your realm, of a term usually applied to the animal kingdom. This term is 'survival of the fittest,' and it refers to Darwin's theory of evolution. Darwin's theory states that those animals of a particular species that are the most adaptable, perhaps with greater strength or some other characteristic, will have a much better chance of surviving and evolving than those beings that may have less bodily strength or are of a smaller size. I wish to tell you that this is falsity and illusion, presented to you by a Human who, though quite brilliant, was mistaken in the evaluation of his own data.

"I would also like to point out that the theory of evolution is, at least in my opinion, more a hypothesis than a theory. I am sure as I say these words that many of your great minds will scoff at the idea that I, a simple Woodchuck, have come to such a conclusion. Perhaps your great scientists would suggest that I return to my university for more study. Why am I even bringing up the theory of evolution? I bring it up to point out that it is an illusion, and this illusion appears in the way you view animals in the physical realm. You see them as your inferiors, though they are, in truth, your relatives, your cousins, and they should be treated with respect and dignity. Now, let us together advance to the core of my lecture. It appears to me that Humans have taken this theory of evolution, or the simple phrase 'survival of the fittest' (though I believe, in this phrase, Darwin's theory has been over-simplified and was perhaps not the thought of the great man himself), from the animal kingdom and laid it upon Human society.

"In your somewhat frightening industrial world, those who have power, either through society or wealth, believe they must control the masses and lord over them, so that the genealogical line of those who are powerful and wealthy will continue to survive and thrive, even at the expense of the less fortunate and the less powerful. In fact, those who have power through politics or wealth, or even through a branch I have left out—religion— believe they have almost the divine right to subjugate others. These powerful few feel they are superior to those poor inferiors below them. They believe it is the duty of the inferiors to support and care for the powerful, while those in power will look after their interests, since this powerful minority feel they know what is best for those poor unfortunates below them.

"I, Professor Woodrow Woodchuck of the animal kingdom, frankly find it quite astounding that, being one of the inferior animals compared to the great wisdom of the Humans, I can yet see the truth of your society. What I see is a dysfunctional, dangerous house of cards that, in the very near future, could tumble down upon your heads. It must be quite embarrassing for you that a member of the animal kingdom can more clearly see how your society truly is than those great minds of your Human realm.

"I have lately been studying one of the most powerful leaders in your world. Frankly, I am frightened. I will not give his name for I do not wish to date this book, but never fear—others like him are likely to follow. This leader and those people who surround him, mostly men, seem to be cut off from the world and thereby have no true foundation upon which to stand. You might think that one who lives in the Faerie world would have no room to talk concerning the thinking of your political leaders in the physical world. However, I would like to point out to you that your leaders themselves live in a fairytale world, but one found in the darker realms.

"Humanity, at this time, is nearing one of the most dangerous cross-roads in all of its history, and it is preparing to enter another time of cata-clysm or Armageddon. For the world to become transformed to a much better, brighter place, Mother Earth and all her children must pass through some dark times, and dark deeds will be done. Before reaching the end of the path to the shining mountaintop, she, with her children, must first pass through the valley of death. Tragically, these terrible times may come about because of men who lust for power and wealth, not only from the people of their own nation, but also from the entire world.

"They are like the famous king Vortigern of the Arthurian legends. He was a usurper, a king who seized his power by treachery and murder. At the end of his wicked reign, he had cut himself off from the land and his people. He no longer knew how they felt, but was concerned only with the gratification of his own evil desires, which he achieved through the tears, blood, and death of his own people. This great tyrant, in an effort to escape the justified wrath of his people, attempted to build a great tower. He wished this tower to stand high upon the mountaintop, high above his people, that he might dwell in its upper chambers unmolested, looking down upon his people and hurling torments from the skies above.

"Of course, there is more to the story than I am telling you here. If you wish to learn more of Vortigern, the Usurper, perhaps you should read some of the legends concerning Merlin and his youth. The reason I am bringing up this ancient tale is that it appears Vortigern has returned, and he and his court are building themselves a great tower again, one of ambition and wrongful power. This ruler and his companions plan to build this terrible, dark tower above their land, laying waste to their land through industry, so that they may gain more wealth and more power. The beautiful forests and green hills and the people themselves will be laid low, their very essences transformed from living beings and ground into fuel to feed the monstrous machine these men plan to use to conquer the entire world. They claim to have the authority to perform these horrific deeds by the will of God, by the mandate of their people, and for the good of their country. At least that is the story they present to the people of their nation and to the people of the world.

"What I find even more frightening is that the majority of the people of their nation and the majority of the people of the world, and even the animals of the physical world and the trees and rocks and rivers of Mother Earth herself, know that their words are false. They know that their actions are against the Mother and Father; yet no one has the courage to defend Mother Earth and her children. There appears to be no Human hero to stand up for Humanity at this time. We, as a people, whether it be Fair Folk, animal, Human, or any other child of Mother Earth, can only pray for courage to stand up against this growing, horrifying evil. We pray that some hero, most likely a Human, will be awakened by the Mother and Father to stand apart from the enslaved masses and rally the people and the rest of Creation about them to hold back the impending storm; to hold the land itself until the return of our beloved brother, Jesus.

"I hope you will pardon my emotional words, but if we, as simple animals, know the difference between right and wrong, why cannot you Humans know the difference between good action and bad action? It is written within your hearts. The instructions are clear. You truly know within you what is truth and what are lies. Why do you turn from that ability and let some future dictator guide your paths? I, as your companion and child of Mother Earth, ask you to take my paw and join with me and others, Human, animal, Fair Folk, and green beings, to form a shield wall against the terrible war that is to come. Join the Mother and Father's side. Stop worrying so much about material things. The Mother and Father will take care of you. They take care of the birds, the grass, the wildflowers, the animals. Will they not take care of you who most resemble them, whose energy they created?

"It is time to end my lecture. I hope I have made it clear, in the animal kingdom or the realm of the animals, whether it be in your physical world or the spiritual world of Tír na nÓg, we do not abuse our power. We do what we must to survive and to live in harmony with our surroundings. Admittedly, we succeed more in this quest in the spiritual world of Tír na nÓg, but, even in the physical world, the animals do try to live in harmony with Creation. If you truly do see yourselves as rulers of the Earth, please consider following the humble example of your animal kin.

"May your paths lead to wisdom and back home to the embrace of the Mother and Father and that of your brother, Jesus. Most sincerely and with weary affection, I am Professor Woodrow Woodchuck."

Dr. Benjamin Badger

Our next guest is an animal healer, who also is well suited to provide his own introduction.

"With greetings to the realm of Humans, I am Dr. Benjamin Badger. I am a medical doctor in Tír na nÓg. I treat not only animals of Tír na nÓg and sometimes of the Human world, but I also treat the Fair Folk of Tír na nÓg and even some Humans who dwell there. In appearance, I am a Badger who wears clothing. Sometimes you might find me dressed in my doctor's jacket; sometimes in a coat and vest and trousers; and, it is true, sometimes I go *au naturel*, as is proper in some circumstances.

"What can I tell you that you have not already heard previously from my other animal colleagues? Perhaps we could briefly discuss the relationship between animals and Humans and their methods of healing. Let us focus our attention first upon the animals of your realm. Sadly, many of those animals who live in the wild have a much lower life expectancy than the domesticated animals that live under your roofs. Yet you may notice that the animals that live in the wild do have their own methods for healing. I am sure you have seen them, whether it be licking or biting themselves or another animal helping them in the process of healing. Perhaps you have seen them wallowing in mud or some other substance to speed the wound healing. There are different methods.

"You may find this surprising, but the animals in your realm even use the power of prayer to aid in the healing of themselves or others of their immediate family. Their power of prayer can be found within their instinct or their own self-knowledge of the need to call upon a higher power, the Mother and Father, to aid in their healing or, in many cases, to ease them into the next world. The animals of your realm do have unseen allies, at least unseen by Human eyes, and many times unseen by the animals themselves until they are in dire medical need. These allies would be spirit animals such as myself and spirit doctors such as Gnomes, Elves, Sprites, or other healers of the Fair Folk.

"Now let us take a brief look at the domesticated animals. Their life expectancy is much longer, for they are protected by their Human companions (or, as you refer to yourselves, their masters) within your household. Through modern veterinary medicine, many animals with various diseases can be healed, their standard of life enriched, or, in some cases, they can be gently eased into the spirit world. For the most part, the veterinary medicine of the Human world is a blessing to the animal companions, but your animal doctors do go too far at times in their quest to heal a much-loved pet. An animal knows when its natural time has come to pass into the spirit lands, but many times this decision is taken out of the animal's paws and placed in the hands of their master.

"The animals in the wild do not have this problem. When it is their time to go, they know. I do not mean to be cold-hearted here. I am very much for keeping an animal healthy and alive with a high quality of life, whether they be domesticated or wild in the physical realms or one of our own in the spirit realms of Tír na nÓg. The main reason I am speaking to you in this manner is to first present you the options of healing for animals, in contrast to the options of healing for Humans. You see, in the wild, though the animals may have shorter life spans, their lives are still ones of spiritual interaction with their environment. This sense of spirituality is also found within the homes of animals that are domesticated. Thankfully, the animals' spiritual balance between the spirit and physical worlds is basically intact within themselves. It is the Humans who have managed to separate the art of medicine from the spirituality of healing.

"Understand this is a blanket statement I am making. It is not always true. Many doctors and healers in your realm, and patients, for that matter, together maintain or even increase the harmony between the body and the spirit. This applies even more so to those who are passing from their physical bodies to their spirit bodies. Still, when it comes to the art of healing, I must point out that a large majority of Humans and medical practitioners lean more towards the science of the healing, and not the spirituality, so that an imbalance can many times occur within the patient's life. An imbalance already exists within the patient because of the disease; yet, sometimes, even with the healing art of medicine and therapy, though their bodies may heal somewhat, this disease, or the imbalance in their spiritual or physical lives, is still there. In other words, the symptoms are buried, and the disease remains hidden.

"Animals use the instinct of prayer, but Humans seem to bury their instincts and do not listen to their instincts. They subdue their instincts deep in the well of their subconscious. Many patients at some point become merely a vessel or container for many different kinds of medications prescribed by their practitioner, or even various forms of treatment or therapies that may or may not help the patient, but will at least enrich the doctor and the clinic where the treatments are performed. I would like to make a suggestion to you, my Human friend, that when it comes to treating an illness, whether it be one of the mind, one of the body, or one of the spirit, that you depend more upon the instinct of prayer, that deep unbreakable connection between you and the Mother and Father Creator. Through prayer, you can strengthen that connection, so that a greater chance of true healing can occur. Strengthening this connection in a prayerful manner to your Mother and Father Creator is, in fact, the best medicine you can take. Not only do you become a patient in the stages of healing by the Creator, but you also take part in your own healing. You become a healer yourself.

"With medicinal prayer, you can, of course, take other medicines prescribed to you by your doctor or medical practitioner. I think, however, the stronger medicine of prayer will actually increase the potency of the other medicines and therapies offered to you by your physical healers. Though the

Mother and Father and their son, Jesus, are the greatest healers in Creation, they also send out among Creation many other spiritual healers. Be they Angels or beings such as myself, an animal doctor, or Fair Folk or others, many spiritual beings love the Mother and Father and their son, Jesus, and aid them with healing throughout Creation. The idea I have just presented to you may make you uncomfortable, so, of course, you should realize the true healers are the Mother and Father and Jesus. From them, all healing flows. A doctor or medical practitioner or minister or I or any healer in Creation could not heal without their power. In other words, the healers are not the healers. The Mother and Father and Jesus are the true healers. We are merely the vessels of healing.

"As a parting thought as I wind down my counsel with you, through the instinct of prayerful healing, I will say, once again, you can become the healer and the healed. This is what the Mother and Father always meant, for you to take control of your own life. We animals, no matter what realm we live in, know this instinctively. You, yourself, also know this instinctively deep down within you. It is time to allow that healing instinct within you to awaken, so that not only will you be able to heal yourself and your loved ones, but you will also be able to take part in the healing of all Creation. I say, take charge of your own healing. Ultimately, the doctor is not in charge of your healing. You are. Many kind regards and wishes of good health to all of you. With Mother and Father's blessing and Jesus' healing power through you, I wish you well."

CHAPTER XII

The Faerie Creation Story

Gwladys and Henry tell the story of Creation as it is understood among the Celtic Fair Folk.

"In the beginning were the Holy Parents, and they were alone in the void. Like many loving couples, they wanted a child, and so they came together, and, from that union, a child was brought forth. Their firstborn child would one day be known as Jesus or Emmanuel, the Messiah, and he would be born as a Human male in the village of Bethlehem.

"The Holy Parents placed the Child in the great nest of darkness you refer to as space. That he might not be lonely, they created for him the stars, so he would have tiny brothers and sisters to play with, but also light to see. After the birth of the stars, the planets were formed, and the tiny Child of the Holy Parents was comforted greatly by watching the flickering stars and the planets that circled them. Yet the Holy Parents were lonely still, and the Child wanted other brothers and sisters, and so the Angels were created.

"Other life was then placed upon the planets. This life you came to know as the sky and the oceans. Then were the mountains born and all manner of green things, among them trees and grass and flowers and other beauties of nature. The Child and the Holy Parents looked down upon these worlds, and they smiled and felt greatly comforted. Yet they found something still missing, and so they created animals to populate these worlds. The Holy Family watched the animals come to life and play and grow up upon the Earth. They watched them feast upon the living green things and breathe the air of the sky and drink the water from the dew and the streams that were placed in these worlds, and they were greatly comforted. Yet, again, they realized that Creation was not complete, and so they created what you would consider the first people. These people lived in peace for many years, and from them sprang not only the Humans, but also the Gnomes, Elves, and others of the Faerie.

"For many, many eons, there was peace in the Garden, and the Holy Parents and the Child walked among Humankind, and each enjoyed the other's company. Humans knew the language of the Elves and Gnomes and others of the Faerie. They knew the language of all animals that walked upon the Earth and the language of all green things. They could speak to the sky, the ocean, or the waters. Most importantly, however, Humans knew the language of the Holy Parents and the Child, for, you see, in the Garden, there was one language among all living things.

"In those early years of Creation, all children of the Holy Parents lived in harmony, and when we speak of all children, we speak not only of all green things and all animals and all people, including the Gnomes, Elves, and other Fair Folk and Humans, but also the Angels, for they are also the children of the Holy Parents. Not only did the Holy Parents lavish love and affection on all Creation, and especially upon their son who was later to be known as Jesus, but they also asked the Angels to act as nannies in helping to care for and nurture the different peoples of Creation. Most of the Angels, having great amounts of maternal instinct and much of the Holy Mother's love within them, happily consented to help nurture or care for Creation. There was one group of Angels, however, who took offense at such a task, and one of these Angels later came to be known as Lucifer.

"Lucifer was one of the most beautiful Angels in all the heavens. His grace and beauty were such that, when first he was created, his light shone nearly as brightly as that of the Holy Parents and the Holy Child. He grew jealous of the attention given to Humans and even more so of the attention given to the Child. He became incensed with the thought that the Holy Parents loved the Child more than him, for, early in his creation, he had developed one flaw, and that flaw was vanity. Lucifer believed the full attention of the Holy Parents should rest upon him and him alone, not upon the Child, not upon the rest of Creation, and most certainly not upon the peoples below who would later be called Humanity.

"Even then, the early Humans were already getting into mischief which they should not have been getting into, and they were beginning to pull away from their Fair Folk brothers and sisters. When you have a mischievous child, you tend to focus more attention on the mischievous child than you do on the other well-behaved children. Lucifer became enraged at this attention to the Humans, and it was then that the essence of the Holy Parents' love began to leak from him. It began slowly at first, but as his rage grew and a small seed of hate was planted, the tear in his spirit increased, and more of the Holy Parents' love and compassion spilled out. He began to associate himself more with the Holy Father Creator, for he saw power and strength in the Holy Father's actions. After a time, he scorned his Holy Mother Creator's love as weak and offensive and turned his back upon her.

"He tried to win his Holy Father's love by creating creatures of his own, but these creations were monstrosities, and they began to wreak havoc on Creation. The Holy Parents were angry with him for creating these monsters that brought harm to the other children of Creation. They confronted Lucifer on this matter and scolded him, demanding to know why he had done this thing. He declared to them that he had done it to show he was as great as they were. He told the Holy Parents he alone should have their love and devotion, and they should not give their love and attention to all these other sickly beings of Creation to which they had given birth. He informed them further that all Creation except himself was inferior, while he himself was greater even than the Holy Child. The Holy Parents pleaded with him to allow their love to return to him and chase the darkness from the heart of his spirit, but Lucifer refused, claiming he should be the creator, for even then he was greater than they were.

"The Holy Parents mourned the loss of such a bright one, but they also felt betrayed. In their great wrath, they hurled Lucifer and his legions of Angels out of heaven. Plummeting through the vast darkness of space, they came upon the Earth and pierced the surface of the Great Mother's face like a brilliant burning star, causing her great discomfort. From this destruction, vast clouds of smoke arose, and volcanoes sprang to life, raining fire down upon the Earth. Massive tracts of forestland burst into flame from the fiery rivers, and many of Creation's gentle children perished in that onslaught of fire. In the midst of this massive destruction, the Evil One called Lucifer created more monsters, and they wreaked even more havoc upon Creation. Smoke filled the skies and let no sunlight in, adding more numbers to the death toll.

"Were it not for the intervention of the Holy Parents and the Holy Child, Mother Earth would have perished that day, as would all Creation. Had the Evil One succeeded in his murder of Mother Earth, upon her death would have appeared a great empty void which would have pulled all the other worlds and, in fact, all Creation into it, tighter and tighter and tighter, compacting it within the darkness. The darkness, unable to contain its hatred of itself, would have exploded outward in a fiery death, engulfing all life. Instead, the Holy Parents reached down and broke free our gentle Mother Earth from the death grip of the Evil One's talons. They flung him and his fallen Angels back out into the cold vastness of space.

"The Earth, freed from her oppressor, continued in peace for many ages, but the Humans continued to move farther and farther away from the rest of the family of Creation. They said, 'It is much too crowded here. Let us go over to that forest or to these hills and plains and gather our food here.' The Humans began to form into groups, and these groups traveled to distant parts of Creation far away from the Garden. They became separated from the rest of their family, from the Elves and Gnomes and other Fair Folk. They began to forget our common language and how to speak to us. They began to forget how to speak to the animals and to the green things, the trees and the grass, and to the sky and the water. Sadly, and most importantly, they began to forget the language of the Holy Parents and the Child. As they pulled away to form even more distinct groups among themselves, they forgot even how to speak to one another. Some Human tribes remembered some of the language of Creation and particularly the language of the Holy Parents and the Child. Other tribes, however, forgot more and more and could barely even communicate with each other. Eventually, they began to war among themselves.

"It was among these warring tribes that the Holy Mother Creator and the Great Mother Earth were forgotten or seen as a threat, for the Holy Mother and Great Mother always whispered words of peace and compassion and nurturing thoughts to them. Gradually, these warring tribes forgot their Mother and ceased to treat their women as sacred partners. They began to see them only as possessions, no better than the cattle they herded or the other beasts of the fields, as vessels for sexual pleasure, and as a way to populate and create more warriors in their tribe. After warring among themselves, Human leaders or conquerors emerged. After their own land was decimated, they took their people—their warriors and their women and children who were more like slaves or beasts of burden—and came down from out of the mountains and made war on the more peaceful tribes who remembered much of the language of Creation and the Holy Parents. These peaceful tribes were the forerunners of the Tuatha Dé Danaan, also known as the Faerie. They remembered well their Holy Mother and the Great Mother Earth, and they had been living in peace for untold ages."

The First Tyrant

Gwladys and Henry present here a story that took place during the early years of Creation.

"This is the story of a tribe which became the first of the warrior tribes, but it is also the symbolic story of how the warrior tribes were driven from the Garden of Eden. In the beginning, this tribe, as did the other tribes, lived in the Garden. Though they separated themselves from the other Humans and from the Elves, Gnomes, and others of the Faerie, they at first lived in a manner of peace and considered women to be sacred. There was, in this tribe, a woman who became the leader of her people, and the people raised her above all others and made her chieftess of the tribe.

"She had the best interests of her people at heart at first, but soon she began to separate her people into groups. She felt the least blemished or more beautiful or handsome of the people were the more spiritually gifted, and so she selected them as elders for her people and bade the others to become as laborers and serve these elders. From among these elders, she selected a strong male to act as her sacred mate. The woman and the man ruled the people as chief and chieftess, and they thought it only proper for those who acted as elders or leaders of the people to be served by the people, while they, in turn, would serve the people. For a time, they ruled their people in peace, but it did appear to those people who were not within the inner council that they had to do all the difficult day-to-day tasks of the tribe. They became slaves. They would bring to those of the inner council food and drink and would serve them, and always it was the council who was served first and whose needs were met first before the other people.

"The man, after a time, decided that the woman had more power than he did, and he grew jealous. He spoke to her about this matter, but she, not believing him to be serious, laughed in his face, saying, 'Was it not I who picked you from the people to rule as my sacred mate?' Though the man laughed along with her, his heart became filled with hatred. One warm evening, the man and woman walked together along the cliffs near where their tribe gathered. The man moved toward her, as though to embrace her, and then he did fling her from the cliff, and she fell to her death on the rocks far below. He returned to his people, claiming she had fallen, and that, in his grief, he must take many women as his sacred mates to replace her, for she alone, he said, was surely worth many of the women of the tribe. He ruled his tribe as a complete tyrant and within him dwelt no heart of a mother. He began to oppress the females of the tribe and soon took all of them as his mates, so that no men had sacred mates of their own, not even the elders.

"After years of being ruled by the tyrant, there was a young woman who did not wish to become the slave or concubine of this great tyrant. The young man she loved, her sacred mate, grieved at the thought of losing her to the tyrant. They decided to flee from the tribe to the safety of the trees. As they rested there, the young woman was approached by the Evil One, who had shape-shifted himself into the form of a serpent. The serpent spoke to her, saying, 'There is a great tree in the center of the grove, and if you eat of the fruit, you will remember the old ways. You will become a ruler among your people, and you will throw down the male tyrant. You will be able to share this fruit with your mate, and you will both become as wise as the Holy Parents. You will become like gods, knowing both good and evil.'

"Though the young woman may have wanted some power for herself, her greatest wish was for the return of the Great Mother and the memory of the Holy Mother Creator, with the knowledge that it would bring peace and shelter from the great tyrant who was pure male and in whose heart dwelt not the Mother. She ate of the fruit, and, true to what the serpent had said, her memory returned, and the ancient knowledge was no longer forgotten. She brought the fruit to her sacred mate and gave it to him to eat. As the Evil One had foretold, knowledge flooded back to the young man, and he remembered everything, including the peaceful times in the Garden and the love of the Holy Mother.

"Sadly, the young man was afraid of this knowledge, for he had listened too long to the words of the tyrant. He betrayed his sacred mate at that moment, saying, 'It was first a woman who rose to power and abused the law of the Holy Parents. It was because of a woman that we lost all knowl-edge of the old ways and the language of Creation and were cast out of the Garden. She is the reason why the tyrant rules us now. That is why the male must rise up and hold down woman and suppress her, that we may be masters of the earth and follow the laws of the Sky Father, who surely rules over the Holy Mother and the Great Mother Earth.'

"Woman thus became subservient to man, for this confused young woman believed the illusion her mate had created—that women of her kind had caused the great fall and the servitude to the tyrant. She had offered her sacred mate the forbidden fruit of memory of the lost knowledge of Crea-tion, so that the young man might remember the Holy Mother and the

Great Mother, and Earth might become whole once again. Sadly, he rejected that knowledge. Before the fall, Humans lived in peace with Creation. The act of forgetting the Holy Mother and turning their backs upon the laws of the Holy Parents and Creation resulted in the great fall. Though you might say it was because of the lust for power by both sexes, it was not because of a woman.

"The young man and woman did not wish to return to the tribe of the tyrant, and so they joined a peaceful village nearby. Meanwhile, the great tyrant, tiring of the women of his tribe, sought more power. He declared to his people that his sacred mate had not really fallen from the cliff, but had been pushed from it by a man from the peaceful tribe nearby. The tyrant declared war, promising his people they would conquer the other tribe and make them their slaves, so that the new slaves from the peaceful village would treat even the weaker people of the tyrant's tribe as elders.

"Those of the peaceful tribe who had drawn the tyrant's attention were the ancestors of the Tuatha Dé Danaan. They did not then know how to fight, and they were at first unwilling to perpetrate such horror and bloodshed upon their enemies. They sought, instead, to show their warring brothers how much better their lives would be if they could see and understand how to live in peace and learn to know the words of the Holy Parents and Child and the language of Creation. They thought they could settle the matter with offers of peace, and they offered to share what they had with their warring brothers.

"The tyrant and his men disregarded their offers. They attacked and slaughtered them and buried the men and boy children in graves, so that the Holy Parents and the Child might not know of it. Yet the Holy Parents did know of it, for the blood of the innocents slain cried out from the ground. The Holy Parents declared that no one might take vengeance upon these warrior tribes, nor could they be slaughtered, even though they slaughtered others. Instead, they drove the tyrant and his people away from the peaceful tribes and set the mark of Cain upon them. The tribes of the Faerie and other peaceful Humans lived in peace again for many years until the warrior tribes returned once more, completely overwhelming them like the waves of the ocean, until they finally sank beneath the Barbarian hordes.

"When the Human warrior tribes began to attack the peaceful tribes, the Holy Parents realized a great chasm had been ripped open between the Holy Parents and the Child and Humanity and the rest of Creation. As the eons came and went, Humanity became more and more convinced they were the masters of Creation. They focused only on the Father and saw him as a warrior who approved of and condoned their conquests. As the warrior tribes grew larger and larger from conquest, they began to spread across the face of the Earth, swallowing the more peaceful Human kingdoms. The Garden was lost to them, for the Holy Parents and the Child had barred the way by Angels who guarded the pathway into the Holy Garden. This continued into the time of your recorded history, when those kingdoms who remembered the Holy Mother and the Great Mother began to vanish. Their beliefs and their teachings were buried beneath waves of condemnation from those who saw all women as the root of evil, inferior to man and the warrior Father God. You have evidence of this warrior sky Father, not only in the Middle East, but also in Europe.

"The Humans forgot that, though the Holy Father can be a protector and a warrior, he is also compassionate, loving, and a good father. He is a good sacred mate to the Holy Mother, and he does not see his love, his sacred mate, as an inferior woman, but as an equal to himself and the Child, an equal in all Creation. It was as the Holy Family watched the gulf widen between them and Humanity that they began to send down Human prophets to warn Humanity and try to bring them back to the Holy Family. They hoped Humanity would begin to hear once again the voices of the Holy Father and Mother and the voice of the Holy Child. Sadly, the male-dominated warrior tribes would barely listen to the prophets, or they would listen only for a short time until the prophet's death, and then they would forget his teachings. Many of the prophets were slaughtered or killed or sacrificed to the many warrior gods the Humans worshipped. The Holy Family began to realize the only way to close the gap between Humanity, the Holy Family, the Child, and the rest of Creation was to give Humans what they craved, an ultimate sacrifice. They began to send prophets down who spoke of the coming Messiah, the king."

CHAPTER XIII

The Wild Hunt

King Arawn and others of the Fair Folk tell the following story.

"It occurred one night," began the King, "in the middle of a feast in our kingdom, that a Great White Stag appeared in the middle of the court. We knew it was spirit, but it drove the dogs into a frenzy and knocked over tables. We felt we must catch it, so we rushed outside, calling for our Unicorns, and we set out after the Stag. With a blast of horns and a clang of our spears against our shields, we were off. Our attendants ran on foot, charging off into the forest, while we, in our brightest clothing, joined the chase under the light of the full moon. We would almost catch the Stag, but then it would leap ahead of us again. Our great white Hounds with red ears followed, baying their deep throaty cry, and far off in the distance we would catch a shimmer of antlers. After a time, the Stag vanished, and the Hounds returned to us.

"We reflected on this, believing it was no ordinary spirit animal, but something more special, more holy. The great white Stag continued to visit our court time after time over a period of many years. Each time it appeared, our Wild Hunt commenced all over again, but always to no avail."

"One year," said Yurigel, continuing with the story, "we watched the Stag glance toward us one last time before disappearing into the bushes. We saw the light glint off its antlers as it left us far behind, and we felt a shift within our spiritual heart Grails and within our minds. We felt a door opening or a curtain being pulled back. We had always known the Wild Hunt was an act of magic, mystery, and spiritual importance, but, for some unexplained reason, this night it meant much more. Something had shifted inside us and transformed us. When we returned home that night, we could not release the image of the great white Stag from our minds, and we pondered deeply upon what this event portended. For days afterwards, there was no other topic above that of the white Stag; it simmered in our minds like a fever and would not let us go. From the four corners of Tír na nÓg, we called the priests, priestesses, and people of the Grove. Gathering in the great Grove, we asked one another, 'Who is the Stag? Is the Stag another god?' Your Christians today might have called us pagans, for it is true, we were, at that time, still a pagan lot.

"Our dreams whispered to us of possibilities, and, in those dreams, we saw a young man with long dark hair and a beard, a Human. The light of the Holy Parents shone upon his face, a light so bright it blinded us, a light more brilliant than the sun and moon and stars all shining at once. It was as though this bright light was reflected through a thick glass or crystal. Sometimes the images would be distorted, and we could not understand what we were seeing. Before this time, we knew of the Holy Parents, but we did not know of Christ. We suspected there was a first child from them, but we felt that we and all of Creation were their children, so, though we believed in the Holy Parents, we of the Tuatha Dé Danaan did not yet know of our brother, Jesus."

King Arawn again took up the story. "We continued to have dreams and premonitions about this young man. Then, one night, a star appeared in the heavens, a bright star that lingered over a small Human settlement, and we knew the first child of the Holy Parents had been born among the Humans. More than three Magi or wise men visited the baby Jesus, and among them were those of the Elven. We still did not understand what it meant, and we did not understand why anyone would choose to become a Human, especially after dwelling in the presence of the Holy Mother and Father. Through visions and dreams, we watched the young child grow into a young man. Finally, when he became of legal age and was considered a man by those of his culture, we watched as he began his mission."

"It was decided," said Yurigel, "that when Jesus, our brother, began his mission of teaching in the land of Judea, we would send observers or emissaries to watch him. It was decided that the Elves, since they most resembled Humans, should go. We covered our ears with our hair, and we even shape-shifted to some degree (though we still retain many of our Elven features when we shape-shift, for we are vain lot). The Gnomes were also to accompany us, and, because of their small stature, it was thought they could pass for our children. We dressed in the clothing of the area, and the Jews believed us to be Gentiles. Still, we rather unnerved them for we did not cover our eyes or our facial features, and so we did not appear quite as other Humans. Ironically, the Gnomes were easier to pass off as children, for they are so playful, and they can appear quite ageless. Some brave Gnomes during that adventure even shaved off their beards.

"We watched Christ teach in Judea and in Galilee, and we began to understand who he truly was, not only that he was the son of the Holy Parents, but that he was the Messiah. It was at this time, as we watched him, that the Gnomes received permission from the Holy Parents to tell us more of what was occurring. We discovered the Gnomes had known of Jesus for many years, but they had been asked by the Holy Parents and Jesus not to tell us, for we were not ready. Because of this, the Gnomes, being very polite as always, had in fact kept the secret to themselves. We watched Jesus for those three years during his mission, and we knew that this Human was, in fact, the son of the Holy Parents, or the Messiah, the firstborn. We watched as he was crucified by the Humans, and we of the Fair Folk thought the Evil One had won, and there would be no redemption for Humanity or for the rest of Creation."

Here Gwladys took up the story, "Christ suffered pain beyond Human comprehension. Before his appearance before Pilate, he was beaten with sticks and rods. His robe was stripped from him, and he stood naked before soul-less Roman guards, whose main mission was to make him suffer unbearable pain. He was blindfolded and beaten, and they spat upon him. They lashed him with a whip with metal and glass woven into it, and it ripped strips of skin from his body. Normal Humans would have died. They took a helmet of thorns and rammed it into his already-bleeding scalp. The poison of the thorns caused nausea and fevers as they worked their way into his head and into his bloodstream. They put the robe back on him and led him before Pilate. Pilate tried to release him, but the Jews, who in truth were representatives for all Humanity, refused to allow it. The Messiah was forced to drag a huge, wooden cross, while slivers of its wood embedded themselves into the wounds on his back. He was very weak and could not long carry the coarse, heavy, wooden cross, and so the soldiers found a kind man in the crowd to help him carry that unbearable load.

"They roped Jesus' feet to the post and tied his hands to the arm pieces. They hammered huge nails through his palms and feet and roughly dropped the post into the ground. He was alone, with no one there with him but his Mother Mary and Mary Magdalene and some of his followers. When he hung upon the cross, his chest was compressed, so he had to push against the post to rise up in order to breathe. His muscles and bones were pulled from their sockets. It was a slow suffocation. It is bad enough when one is just tied, but with nails, it is nearly impossible.

"His followers gathered at a distance, but his mother, Mary, and Mary Magdalene were at the foot of the cross. His sorely grieving mother tried to reach him to give him water from the Grail Cup to ease his suffering, but he was too high up on the cross. That is what the cup is, a vessel to ease the suffering of Humanity, and Mary, his beloved mother, desperately wanted to use this vessel to ease the suffering of her slowly dying son. Mother and Father God then poured out all the wrath they had felt for thousands of years because of Humanity's deeds, and they turned their back upon Christ, their son. Feeling the terrible loss, he cried out, 'My God, my God, why hast thou forsaken me?' as their great wrath struck his pain-wracked body. In the last moments of his life, Christ, in a hoarse whisper, said, 'I thirst. Please give me a drink.' The Roman soldiers offered him vinegar on a sponge, attached to a long stick, to wet his lips. Finally, he died.

"The Romans came with hammers to break his legs, so he would be unable to support himself to draw breath. This was often done for prisoners, so they would suffocate more quickly. They were not sure if Jesus was yet dead, so they stabbed his side with a spear, and living water poured out. They knew then that he was dead, and they took him down. Joseph of Arimathea gave up his family tomb, and there Christ was laid to rest."

Continued King Arawn, "The Great Mother Earth was wracked with sobs at his death. She ripped herself open and was split, and the Earth shook and trembled in a great quake, even unto Tír na nÓg. The sky turned dark with grief, a darkness with no light within. Though it was noontime, it became darker than midnight. We thought it was the end of all Creation at that very moment, and we left and began to travel back to our realm. As our small group of Elven and Gnomes passed through the City of Jerusalem, we saw, walking through the streets, those of the dead. They had climbed from their graves, and many of the Humans that day saw family members who had long been dead walking about, hale and hearty, crying 'Why have you done this? Why have you crucified the Son of God, the Messiah?'

"We returned to our realm, but, even in Tír na nÓg, for the first time in our memory, the skies were filled with black clouds, and no sunlight pierced them. We gathered together and waited for the end."

"I must say here," Yurigel added, "that the Gnomes knew in their hearts, or had a feeling, that this was not the end. Most of the rest of us of the Fair Folk, however, had given in to despair, grieving the loss of our Human family. We thought that with Jesus' death, the Holy Parents would have no choice but to completely destroy Humanity, for had Humans not killed their firstborn child, our brother, the brother to all Creation?"

"After three days," continued King Arawn, "a bright light broke through, and joy began to fill our hearts, though we did not understand why. We were most grateful that it appeared the Holy Parents were going to spare us and spare Tír na nÓg. When the sunlight pierced the clouds, we all rushed out from our homes, our burrows, and began to praise the Holy Parents and thank them for sparing us. It was then we heard the horns sound for a Gathering of the Grove, and we began to fill the Grove. Standing there in the center, we found our priestesses and priests. With tears of joy in their eyes, they informed us that Jesus, the Messiah, had risen from the dead, that death could not hold him, and he had defeated the Evil One.

"Though we did not see him rise personally, we believed it to be true, for the priestesses and priests had seen it in a vision, some while they slept, and others as it was happening. All of us, in fact, dreamt of the event, some more clearly than others. Rhiannon and I each had a dream of a stone being rolled away and a bright light shining from a dark cave. I first thought I had dreamt of the moon eclipsing the sun, and then a giant hand from heaven rolled the moon away, thereby freeing the sunlight to fall upon all of Tír na nÓg. It was not until later that we understood the intent of what had happened. Even then, we did not fully understand why Jesus had allowed himself to be crucified by Humans and to die on the cross, when he could have called ten thousand Angels to come to his rescue at any time.

"It was a year later, around May-time, and we were feasting in our hall, when the Stag appeared to us once more. We quickly gave chase. Flying past Humans on many continents, we pursued the Stag throughout the night. The Unicorns trailed vapor from their nostrils, and the Hounds bayed. We, in our armor, sounded our war horns. Finally, the Stag stopped upon the Hill of Golgotha, the hill upon which Christ was crucified. There were but a few Humans about, and they quickly scattered, thinking we were the devil's children."

"The great white Hounds," Gwladys continued, "had surrounded the Stag, but they did not attack, for it was never in their interest to harm the Stag, but only to detain it, so that the Elven might speak with it. It was then that the Stag stood up upon its hind legs and transformed into the image of Christ. They saw in the young man's eyes great compassion and love, more than was ever felt before. By dwelling in the realm closest to the Holy Parents, the hearts of the Elven had become filled with compassion and love, but when they gazed into the eyes of this young Human, their hearts were filled with an overwhelming love, and they knew him to be the Messiah. He vanished then in a great blinding light, and the High King and Queen of the Elves realized the Great White Stag would never be a mystery to them again, for now they had come to know him for who he truly was."

King Arawn spoke once more. "In that moment, Rhiannon and I were born again and became Christians, as did our subjects. In my kingdom, all saw and chose to become Christians.

"We still chase the Great Stag once a year. It is a symbol, not only of Christ, but also of the Great Mother and Father. As we chase the Stag across the Human Earth, and it takes different paths along the Earth, we perform a symbolic, ritual ceremony. We allow the spiritual energy to flow through us, and this energy disturbs the air. Our brightness, and that of our Unicorns and Hounds, drives back the Evil One's minions and holds them at bay, for we travel to the darkest spots on the Earth. Our Wild Hunt ends each year in a grove of trees where the Great Stag waits for us. The grove is a sacred, mysterious spot, which is being threatened like all else on the Great Mother Earth. We commune with the Stag, and the Stag becomes Christ. We hope that by doing this each year, we will set in motion the energy, spark, revolution, change, or revival of the Human spirit. When we first began the Wild Hunt long ago, it was out of a sense of mystery, but now, though we may startle some in our passing, we harm no one, and our hearts are filled only with compassion and love."

Seeking Heaven

Following is a compilation of several talks with the Fair Folk, especially with Gwladys and Henry. This information did not come to us in a smooth way, for these teachings on sin, karma, and reincarnation are quite different from what we were taught when we were younger. Though we found it difficult at first to surrender our own preconceptions, we have come to believe that what is presented here makes sense if one accepts that the Mother and Father truly love and care for their children and wish to give them every possible chance in life.

Long before the coming of Christ, the Evil One used the concept of sin as a shield wall to prevent Humans from knowing the love of the Holy Parents. Those who believe they are without sin persecute those who behave contrary to their beliefs of how things should be; yet the sins of the persecuted are often less than those who sit in judgment upon them. The Pharisees have returned, self-righteous, but filled with dead men's bones.

One who believes he is unworthy because of his sins may turn away from the Holy Parents and surround himself with a dark fog. This fog is made up of the shame and sadness he feels when he remembers his own sinful acts. He comes to believe the lie whispered to him by the Evil One, that the Holy Parents can never love a sinner. Though a person may once have committed murder or other fearful acts, such past actions do not necessarily make him bound for Hell. Due to the grace of the Mother and Father's love, and because of Christ's sacrifice on the cross, a person can be transformed, reborn into a life of love and light. One who has done great wrong can become so changed through the love of the Holy Parents that he later performs great acts of good. Religious beliefs are not the deciding factor in a person's spiritual fate. It is the relationship a person has with God that is important. The Mother and Father are far more merciful and forgiving than we can ever imagine.

The Evil One's portrayal of karma and reincarnation is as flawed as his portrayal of sin. When a soul returns to the spirit realm, he is met by higher beings, who help him review his life and see where he chose the lower path. No one is forced to leave the spirit realm and be reborn on Earth, but, of their own free will, many spirits choose to reincarnate on Earth to try to make amends for past misdeeds. If they did evil in one life, they will often do better in the next life.

Imagine if you will that in a previous life on Earth, you murdered some-one. Even though you committed murder, you still did enough other good deeds during your life that the good within you outweighed the evil. The evil within you was destroyed upon your death when you passed through the tunnel of light to heaven. There you were met by an angelic being, and you reviewed your life. Some time later, you decided you wished to return to Earth to try to atone for the murder you had committed. You vowed to return and sow the seeds of good, so there would be that much less evil in the world. The Evil One did not wish you to do good, for his plan is to fill the world with evil. When you returned to Earth in another body, he sent dark ones against you, and you were murdered. You were not murdered as a karmic repayment for the sin of committing a murder in your past life. You were murdered solely to prevent you from doing good.

The Evil One lives by the Law of Karma, a law that he created. It is not a law of the Holy Parents, for, in the realm of the Holy Parents, there is only love, not retribution. The Evil One thought Christ would not allow himself to be crucified. He believed he would refuse to be sacrificed and would save himself, or, if he died, then that would be the end of it. It was a foolish notion, for Christ was there long before the Evil One, so how could he destroy someone eternal? Even though Christ was crucified, and the Holy Parents poured their wrath out upon their own son, Christ triumphed by arising from the dead. He entered Hell to free those who did not belong there, so they could return to the Holy Parents, absolved of their sins. The Evil One will encourage you to water the seeds of evil and negativity, but know now that you can choose to transform them to light. Do good, no matter if you have done evil before, for you can be transformed.

We wish to add one note of caution here. In the days to come, when the Evil One rises to power, those who survive will be urged to accept a form of identification that has come to be known by many Christians as the "mark of the beast." We believe this mark will be in the form of a miniature computer chip embedded in the hand or in the forehead. The area of the chip may also be marked with an attractive tattoo with a number woven into it for further identification. Those who accept this mark will do so knowingly, with the awareness they are pledging their allegiance to the Evil One. Though the mark may allow them to acquire material goods for a short time, it will also seal their fate, and they will forever lose their chance to enter heaven. We tell you this now and urge you to nurture your own spiritual strength, so that in the future you may see clearly and choose wisely should this choice come before you.

The Holy Grail

Gwladys speaks now of the true meaning of the Grail Cup.

"This is a brief story of Jesus and one of the many events that occurred during his Earthly ministry. Jesus was sitting by a well in hot, dusty Samaria, and he was thirsty. His disciples had been gone for some time in search of food and lodging. A Samaritan woman came to draw water. She had a good heart and was more spiritually advanced than many of the Pharisees of the day, but she was looked down upon, because she was a

Samaritan and a woman who had had several husbands. Jesus asked this woman for a drink of water. Now, you must understand, the Jews did not associate with the Samaritans in those days, and they were treated with little or no respect. The woman looked at Jesus in amazement. She asked him why he would wish to receive water from her, since she was a Samaritan and considered unclean.

"Jesus replied that if she would ask him for living water, she would never thirst again and never die. The woman, still not understanding, asked him who he was that he could offer her this living water. Jesus told her he was the one of whom her prophets had spoken. He helped her to understand that he offered the gift of the living water of eternal life, that she might be reborn and freed from the chains of karma or sin. If she accepted the cup of living water from Jesus, she need never reincarnate on Earth again, but would become, at that moment, a spiritually evolved being, who would never be bound by karmic chains again.

"The Holy Grail has always existed. Before the foundations of this Earth were set, the Grail existed. It was the vessel into which the Mother and Father God poured their love. Before time itself existed, Christ was born to Mother and Father Creator, and yet, before his birth, the Grail existed.

"The Mother Goddess took it upon herself to give birth to Creation in her womb, though it took both the Mother and the Father to create the first seed of life. The Mother's womb is the original Grail Cup, as later reflected in the basin where the original primordial life was born upon the Earth. The Holy Child was the first part of Creation to be born, and the rest of Creation followed. The birth of spirit, or the Holy Child, came from the Holy Parents. Then all three wove and created spirit-matter using earth, air, fire, and water, and Creation passed from spirit to spirit-matter. When Humanity chose to draw away from the rest of Creation, they pulled the physical side of the Great Mother Earth with them, at least in their own minds, and the Earth became more matter-spirit. In the days to come, when the physical Earth and the spirit Earth merge once more, the Earth will return again to spirit-matter.

"The Holy Grail first appeared upon the Earth as a depression within the earth of the Great Mother. It was not made by an object from space or by the crown of Lucifer, nor by his physical striking of the Earth. One might say it was a depression created by the Holy Mother and Father, a great basin of rock bordered by earth. From this basin, the first waters sprang forth, and the first oceans came to be. It was the original fountain from which all life arose. This depression was located in an area between the British Isles and America.

"After a time, the more peaceful children of the Holy Parents were forced to retreat before the encroaching Human Barbarian hordes. They cried out to Mother Goddess and Father God for a vessel they could carry with them. Their pleas were granted, and the depression in the Earth was transformed into a large, metal cauldron, which could be transported from place to place. The vessel carriers then were both Human and Fair Folk. Thus, from a rock basin, a depression carved by the Holy Parents within the womb of the Great Mother Earth, the Grail was transformed into a pure metal container that would never rust. This container was made from a metal Humans will never discover and which even we of the Faerie cannot make.

"The Holy Grail was once the cauldron of immortality. The vessel could be used to prepare the peoples' food, and it would nourish both body and spirit, but it was also a vessel for healing. When the waters of the Great Mother were placed in the cauldron and then given to those who were wounded or sick, the waters would heal them. If one of the dead was placed within the vessel, he would be brought back to life.

"At the time of Christ's birth, his godmother, the Holy Mother Brighid, sought a suitable vessel for her godson to use as a drinking cup. In answer to her prayers, the Holy Parents caused the cauldron to be transformed into a simple drinking cup. This cup was brought by Holy Brighid herself from the land of Faerie and was held by Brighid as she helped Mary care for Jesus and her other children. The rim of this same cup was held to Jesus' lips by his mother when he was given liquid by her as a child. It is this cup that Brighid now cares for at her Holy Well, where sometimes the lucky ones of Humanity may visit her. She blesses them and gives them living water to drink from the Holy Well, held within the vessel of the Holy Grail itself.

"Though this wooden cup would appear to be in a humbler state than when it appeared as a cauldron, it is in its most pure form. It is the same cup offered to Jesus by his Mother Mary when he thirsted upon the cross, but he could not reach to drink from it. This cup caught drops of his living blood as he hung upon the cross, and his blood mingled with the water held within the cup. The mixture of Christ's blood and the living water of the Holy Parents seeped into the molecules of the wood, and the cup was transformed into the sacred cup you refer to as the Holy Grail. In its transformation, it became the fourth element—air or spirit—for Christ's blood transformed it to its most pure form.

"In each stage of the Grail's transformation, all four elements are combined. Water, fire, and earth were already present when the depression of rock was carved out by wind or the element of air. The metal cauldron was formed using earth, air, fire, and water, and all four of those elements are present in the wooden cup. The Grail Cup represents the Great Tree whose roots bury themselves deep in Mother Earth. The Tree needs the sunshine or fire to grow, for it receives energy from the sun. The Tree also needs water to survive and air to breathe, which releases carbon dioxide. Taken together, these make up the wood cup; in spirit, all is there.

"Christ was the only one of his kind. The religions of old spoke of his coming and predicted it. He came at a focal point in history; had he had not come, Humanity would not still exist. Had he been born a woman and crucified, because of the patriarchy that existed at that time, you would never have heard his name. Both Humans and animals were sacrificed to the old gods, and their priests knew when Christ came, blood would be demanded, for Humans were accustomed to blood sacrifice. The Grail Cup also represents the cup Christ held in his hands at the Last Supper, when he said it was his blood he would have to shed because of the hard-heartedness of Humanity. It was the water offered to the woman at the well to return to Mother Goddess and Father God. It represented life's sparkling waters, but Humans demanded death instead. Had Humanity accepted the cup of life, the Earth would have been made whole, and life would have been paradise, but Humans chose the sacrifice instead.

"Christ hoped when he began his mission that Humankind could be turned around, but he knew he would have to die. In the Garden of Gethsemane, he prayed that the cup of sacrifice would be taken away from him, for all of Mother and Father God's wrath for what Humanity had done was about to be poured down, and it would not be just upon Humans, but upon all Creation. He knew that by drinking from the cup of sacrifice, that wrath meant for Humanity would be taken into himself, so that Creation might be spared. He prayed he would not have to suffer so. He was so afraid that drops of blood came from his pores, and he wept and shook. His followers had fallen asleep, and he realized he was truly, truly alone.

"The Evil One believed that if the Messiah, the one known as Jesus, could be crucified and killed, he would have triumphed over the Holy Parents and would become the creator and ruler of the Great Mother Earth.

He believed, in his arrogance, that he would become a god. After his crucifixion, Christ lay in the tomb for three days, and, in that time, he met the Evil One. He broke the chains of death and descended into Hell, the land of the dead. The Evil One had created there an illusory heaven to entrap many of those who departed the physical Earth at the time of death. Those who entered this fraudulent heaven, in reality a Hell, would never come to know the far greater heaven awaiting them in the realm of the Holy Parents. This land of the Evil One's creation held Pagans, Jews, and those of other religions. When Christ came, they saw the Great Light, and he led them out. He freed the Evil One's prisoners from the dark pit and smashed down the gates of Hell. He broke their shackles and told them they were never to return. The light he brought was so great that, from that day forward, Hell could be a home only for the Evil One and his minions.

"Mother and Father God agreed never again to turn their backs upon Humanity. Their love, which is greater than all the light of the sun and stars combined, filled their son's broken body and healed the nail holes in his hands and feet. When the stone was rolled away, a great light blinded the Roman soldiers, who fell down upon their knees as though dead, for Christ had risen. His mother, Mary, and Mary Magdalene were first to believe he lived again, before any of the male disciples were convinced. Peter was the rock upon which the church was built, but the Marys were the earth upon which it rested.

"We of the Faerie saw this take place. We marveled at how Humans could be so blind as to crucify the son of the Holy Parents. We could not understand how they could choose the cup of wrath instead of taking the cup of love. Christ took the cup of wrath that would have destroyed Humanity and much of the Earth. Never again will Mother and Father God let that much wrath descend. Their wrath may come, but it will not totally consume or destroy, for Christ will show the Holy Parents the scars from the nail holes in his hands, and he will act as an intermediary for Humans and remind his Parents of their promise.

"Christ died for all of Earth, but mostly for Humanity. He took the cup of wrath the Humans mixed themselves. They chose that Christ should drink from their own poisonous brew rather than the cup of eternal light and life and salvation. This is not a cup dependent upon one's faith or religion. It is a cup given to all life, not just Humanity. Humans handed him the cup of wrath, for perhaps their collective unconscious thinking was 'better him than us.' Many Human churches now think that only if you drink from their definition of the cup of salvation will you be saved, but that is not true. The Grail Cup is for all Humanity.

"After Christ's death and resurrection, the cup was held by Mary, the Mother of Jesus. Upon her death, it was given to Joseph of Arimathea, who, along with Mary Magdalene, traveled with the cup to Glastonbury in Britain. For a time in Britain, there were two Glastonburys, one physical and one spiritual. The Grail receded eventually into the spiritual Glastonbury.

"The Holy Grail is now a simple, wooden cup with no gems embedded in it; yet it shines more brightly than any gem found on the surface of the Earth. Nothing Humanity can find or create will equal the Grail, for it shines with the love of the Father God and the Mother Goddess and the Holy Child Jesus and Mother Mary. It shines so brightly because, though the Grail Cup is more precious than anything found on Mother Earth, its contents are even more precious. It holds the living water for all Humanity, the water from which all life flows. That living water is the love of the Holy Family. The staff we carry as priestesses and priests reflects the Holy Father, and the cup reflects the Holy Mother, so that one or the other may not be forgotten in the minds of the children of Creation."

The Great Tree

Gwladys and Henry speak of the Great Tree in Tír na nÓg and what it symbolizes.

"Before the Christ child was born, our Gnome elders saw the birth of a Human, who would become a Great Tree, which would appear in the center of our Grove. He would be the tree of life, a tree that would once again close the chasm between the Holy Parents, the Great Mother Earth, Humanity, and the rest of Creation. The Human prophets referred to him as the lamb and the great king. We of the Faerie saw him as the Great Tree and the great King of Creation. Our elders saw that it was quite likely this child would be sacrificed upon a tree, which again would symbolize the Great Tree in our Grove.

"The Great Tree was born as a twig at Christ's birth, and, during his life, it was always a sapling. At the end of Christ's life, he hung upon a cross suspended between heaven and earth. The cross upon which he was crucified was like the trunk of a tree, with its roots buried deep in the womb of the Great Mother Earth and its limbs reaching high, suspended above the

Earth, to touch the face of the Holy Parents. Upon his death, the Great Tree wilted, its leaves fell off, and it appeared that it would die itself. Upon Christ's resurrection, it sprang to life and grew leaves, and birds landed in it and began to sing.

"Christ appeared at the foot of the tree, which was then not much taller than he. We were blinded by his brilliance and his love and compassion. He said he had done the will of the Holy Parents, and now the chasm between Creation and the Holy Parents had been closed. No longer could sin and the evil deeds of Creation hold Humans from the loving embrace of the Holy Parents. All Creation had returned to the Holy Parents, as a prodigal child returns to her parents, who, seeing her at a great distance, run to her and embrace her. Though the child may prostrate herself at the feet of the Holy Parents, she will be picked up and embraced, given a fine set of clothing, and brought into the house, where great feasting will begin in honor of the return of the child.

"Christ spoke again, and he told us he would sit beside the Holy Parents to remind them of what he had done. When the Evil One accuses the children of Creation, especially of Humanity, of an evil deed, Jesus will remind the Holy Parents that he died for every evil deed that Humans have committed or will commit, and he will remember the Human's name and tell it to the Holy Parents. Then, as he raised his arms and signaled he was to return to the Holy Parents, he was lifted up from us and became brilliant light, and his form blinded us with the light of a million suns. As he rose up from our realm, we could see the light of compassion and love in his eyes. He called to us by name, and we each heard our very own name spoken aloud as he called to us.

"The small thin sapling began to grow and grow and grow, so that finally, when we could see Jesus no more, in his place stood the Great Tree, the tallest tree ever to grow in our realm. Its roots are buried deep in the womb of the Great Mother, and its limbs reach high to the realm of the Holy Parents to caress their faces with love. I, Gwladys, and my sacred mate, Henry, do tell this tale as it happened, for we were there and saw it with our own eyes and heard our names spoken by Jesus, the Messiah.

"The Great Tree, to us, symbolizes and is a reflection of the one you refer to as Christ or Jesus. It draws together the Holy Parents and all their children of Creation into a tight embrace, so that the gap between them and their children exists no more. Only in Humanity's mind does this chasm still exist, for they are fed lies by the Evil One, and these lies dwell even in their teachings and in their churches. Jesus gave his life and became the savior for all Creation to close that gap. He thwarted the plans of the Evil One, but the Evil One refuses to acknowledge he has already lost. He continues to fill the minds of Humanity with propaganda and lies, in the hope they will still turn the tables in his favor.

"The Great Tree in our Grove shelters and protects us and gives us all manner of fruit to eat. It is the location where we hold many of our most sacred ceremonies. It is at the base of this giant tree, in front of the massive roots, that Jesus himself appears, many times with Mother Mary, to speak with us. It is at these roots where many times the travelers who have gone on to the realm of the Holy Parents are found sitting, waiting for their students to come to them. When we see this tree, we see Jesus, the Messiah, or the Christ. This is why our priestesses and priests, our elders, carry the wooden staff, for it is seen as a reflection of the Great Tree, and the Great Tree is seen as a symbol for Christ or Jesus.

"Christ purified and transformed those Human spirits he rescued from the land of the dead, and he brought them to the realm of the Holy Parents, born again and white as snow. This is the Holy Parents' wish, that all Humanity will be born again and transformed, that the Evil One may have none of them, and that they will dwell in the land and in the house of the Holy Parents. Yet the war goes on. We believe in our hearts as many Humans believe, for we have seen the future when the Evil One will fall. There will come a time when he will rise no more, and his evil will become a memory, forgotten by all Creation.

"We understand that the Holy Parents' wish, and the wish of Jesus and of Mary, was never that Humanity would be separate from Creation, but instead would be a part of it. The Holy Parents take great comfort in all Creation and see all Creation as their relations. They grieve at what Humanity does to their daughter, the Great Mother Earth. The Holy Family grieves at what Humanity does to every green thing and to the animals, the air, and the water. They grieve that Humanity appears to have but a single intent and that is, like their grandfather, Cain, to kill Creation, so they may become its masters. But how can you be a master of something that is dead? If Humanity succeeds in destroying or murdering all Creation, they them-selves will die, for they are part of it. If a small child who is too young to care for itself kills its mother and father, will it not also die? Humanity is too young to care for itself, and by killing the Great Mother Earth and all Creation, they will surely also die.

"Woven within our spirit teachings is the reflection of the Holy Parents and the reflection of the Child and of Mary and the acknowledgment that we are part of the family of Creation and the children of the Holy Parents. We are brothers and sisters to Jesus and Mary, and we must learn to live in harmony and recognize that kinship and spirit we have with all Creation, with life itself. This is why our ceremonies reflect all these things and reflect the kinship or the harmonic relationship we have with our family, the Great Mother Earth and her children, and the very stars and other world planets themselves. Most importantly, our ceremonies reflect the acknowledgment that there is no gap between us and our Holy Parents, who love us very, very much, and there is no gap between us and the Child, who died for us that we might live. We are held tight in the loving arms of their embrace, and it is this message that we wish to bring to Humanity."

CHAPTER XIV

Wulf and the Council of Twelve

Wulf is an animal spirit guide. Although we have spoken with other animal spirit guides, his words touch on a subject we wish to explore in this chapter and that is the future of Humanity and Mother Earth.

"We are the Wolves of the Elven lands of light, otherwise known as the Hounds of Tír na nÓg or the Faerie Hounds of the Great Hunt. You have already been taught elsewhere in this book of the benefits of experiencing the comradeship of a spirit animal companion. Therefore, I, Wulf, Chieftain of the Hounds of King Arawn and Queen Rhiannon, will not dwell too long on this subject. Whatever spirit animal comes to work with you, there should be a feeling of mutual kinship between you and this animal. Whether the animal be a noble Eagle, a proud Lion, a strong Bear, a loyal Wolf, or another animal, such as a small, meek Mouse, we each have our own gifts. We all have powers that have been gifted to us by the Mother and Father Creator.

"You will find that the gifts given to the spirit Wolves by the Mother and Father Creator are the ability to be trustworthy guides who can successfully lead you through the dark wilderness within your heart, but also help guide you through the wastelands of your physical world. You will find a spirit Wolf who serves the Holy Family to be loyal, filled with wisdom, playful, and a fine hunter of the spiritual things that have been lost in your life. Again, these are merely the gifts we possess. You will discover, as I have spoken of earlier, that each animal has his or her own set of many gifts given to them by the Mother and Father Creator. Our main purpose as spirit Wolves is to serve the Mother and Father and our beloved king and brother, Jesus, through service to the High Elven King and Queen, Arawn and Rhiannon of Tír na nÓg.

"Part of our duty and tradition, on the night of Samhain or October 31st, is to cross the heavens with our King and Queen and the other Fair Folk of Tír na nÓg. Since this tradition is described elsewhere in these pages, I will speak here of our other duties. My duty is to act as a companion friend to Lili, the Lady of the Lake, who now resides in Human body, while my lovely wife, Luna, acts as a helpmate to Merlin, also residing in Human body at this time. Though many Wolves reside in Tír na nÓg, Luna and I belong to a smaller council referred to as the Council of Twelve. Ten other Wolves are part of this council. One Wolf is a companion to King Arthur, who has been reborn in this time. Another one of our company is companion to his lovely Queen Gwenhwyfar, who, like Arthur, has been reborn. The other Wolves are companions to the others of Arthur and Gwenhwyfar's inner circle. Obviously, Arthur has and will have more than just eleven companions, but our small Council of Twelve, with the twelve Humans, will be twelve small seeds to bring about vast and wonderful change, a force for good in a time of terrible darkness and Earth changes during these last days of your Human reality."

The Days to Come

The words that follow come from a series of visions concerning the future of Mother Earth and her Human children.

I am in a forest with a cloak flung about my shoulders and my staff in my hand. I come to a body of water, and I gaze down into it. Then I kneel at the edge of the water, resting my staff upon the ground as I peer more closely into its depths. A salmon swims over the heavenly body reflected in the water, a bright full moon. I see buildings, tall splinters of their former glory, blackened, charred, their windows smashed. Cars sit abandoned in the street, blackened and skeletal. Thick, grey dust and bones are every-where.

The sky is not normal. It looks like the Aurora Borealis. The clouds change color from white to green to red. It is raining shards of glass. I hear it tinkling as it strikes the buildings, hammers the buildings, and shatters on the broken concrete. It dents the cremated remains of cars and explodes the skulls that lie scattered on the ground. All the Human forms look the same, grey in color with blunted features. I see the form of a woman sitting on a bus stop bench. I can see the vague shape of hair, eyes, nose, chin, and shoulders. She sits with her hands placed firmly upon her legs, feet close together. I think her head is slightly bowed as if in prayer. I touch her form, and it disintegrates to ash, carried away with the wind. I do not know if it is truly raining shards of glass or of ice.

The moon rises in this realm. It is huge and not at all like a typical moon rising. It is a massive half moon, but where a half moon would ordinarily appear shaded horizontally, this moon seems to be shaded vertically. Then I realize that the lower half has been nearly bitten off, with a jagged edge remaining. The moon rises through the boiling clouds. Stars appear, burn brightly, and go out. I do not know what city this is. I think it is many cities.

I walk through the desert over wind-blown sand. It is daytime now. I see houses, just the tops of them, rising up out of the sand. It appears these houses have been buried by sand, for I am walking almost level with their roofs on the surface of the desert. I come upon what seems to be a large lake in the desert. I think it is covered by ice at first, but then I realize I am looking at a sheet of glass that goes on and on, spreading outwards. A skeletal metal structure rises up, and cars, many of them, have merged with and melted into the glass. I think I see people beneath the glass, pressed up against it, the sand pushing against their backs. It is almost like seeing insects trapped in amber. I think this town may be Los Angeles.

The sea is red and sluggish, and it stinks. I am on the beach now, the city behind me. Many whales are beached upon the shores. Their spirits are gone, but their rotting carcasses and skeletons remain. The sea smells of death. Even in daytime, the clouds boil. The sun shines weakly through them, and they change color, sometimes gray or white or red or green. Sometimes in this desert, I see red sand mixed in with the other sand. I do not know if there was red dust in the city where I earlier stood, for it was dark, and it seemed as though it had rained earlier in the night there.

I have left the dark and melted city behind me now, and I stand upon a hill in a place far from the desert lands, though it has its own scars to bear. The trees here are scorched to blackened stumps all around me, and I see the carcasses of animals, so burned that almost nothing but their shadows remain. Above me, the sky is cloudy, but it does not boil or change color. It is gloomy, and rain is coming. In this charred, blackened landscape, I stare across what looks like a great pit of red clay. Miles away, I can see giant cavities gouged out of the earth, as if heavy machinery had been moving earth and digging up the red clay, but I do not think the holes were caused by machinery. In the distance, were I to walk across the red clay, I would come to the beginning of red cliffs with a green field atop them. From the dead forest hill where I now stand, I see the beginning of mountains with green trees that appear healthy. A red ocean crashes against red cliffs. Interstate 40 struggles out of the waves and through the mountain pass. A great stone wall and gate bar the passage along the highway.

Ocean waves batter against the cliffs. The ocean is red, and the stench of death it carries even reaches up here, though it is worse in many other areas of the country. Sometimes those who live here are fortunate, and the wind blows the death smell away. Not here by these cliffs, but in other places, the ocean rolls in, sluggish and thick, almost like gelatin. Brackish and moving slowly like a swamp, the ocean in those places has remained spoiled and rotten. By the side of these cliffs, at least, the ocean has become cleaner in weeks or perhaps in months. It was very bad at first, but it has become better. In some areas, however, the ocean will recover only after Jesus' return.

The sky overhead is clear now, but terrible storms sometimes roll in. In certain parts of the country, the sky remains black and boiling. Giant bolts of lightning streak down, blasting holes into the ground. Quakes come, the earth opens, and towns plunge into pits of fire or into dark holes, never to be found again. Volcanoes erupt and explode with lava. Sometimes lava is seen within the ocean, fire, gray with a mixture of red. Some areas of the country look like red deserts, covered in dried lava and red dust mingled together. The forested areas suffer. Pine and fir trees seem to do better, although hardwood trees with leaves do still survive within our forests. Sometimes it appears they are going through winter, but days of green buds still come.

We communicate sometimes by radio, when the sky permits, with communities across the United States; sometimes even across the world, but mostly across the United States. Some communities are frantic. They have not fared well, and their people are just trying to hang on. Some communities are doing better. Like us, they have a growing season and can actually grow food after a time, perhaps after the first year. It seems we were invaded by an Asian nation, perhaps China. On the West Coast, I see remnants of their troops and weaponry. I see a red flag, torn upon the ground.

The Red Dragon of the East fights the Red Dragon of the West. The Red Dragon of the West flees before the Red Dragon of the East. The Red Dragon of the East thinks it is cowardice, but the Red Dragon of the West flees the approaching storm that forms behind the Red Dragon of the East's back, unleashed by its own people. The Red Dragon of the East perishes upon America's Western lands. The Red Dragon of the East perishes in the Middle East. The Red Dragon of the East perishes in its own lands. The Red Dragon of the West is scalded, wounded. It becomes the Green dragon, and, where its red blood touches, where its scales fall off, here and there appear green places, green meadows, and green trees. Crops grow, as it makes its way across the broken land.

The people of the South, Brown Eagle of the South, cannot cross the terrible foreboding waters to the land of the Green Dragon, to the land of the Eagle. To the North of the Green Dragon's lands, the land of the Eagle, the northern lands contain pockets of survival, but other areas are covered with a sheet of thick, thick ice. The people of Alaska are no more. Ice covers the land of Canada and crosses the border to the land of the Green Dragon. Ash and fire lie beneath a mile of ice. The lands of the South become colder, like the lands of northern Europe a thousand years ago. Crops still grow in the short growing season. The Ten-Headed Dragon crosses the ocean of death to fight the Green Dragon. It begins to sink in blood as it touches the shores of the Green Dragon. The sea scorches the heads and the feet of the Ten-Headed Dragon with the tail. The Ten-Headed Dragon does much damage and wounds the Green Dragon, but then it turns and flees. The Green Dragon spews fire upon the Ten-Headed Dragon. Scorched, it returns home to spout lies of victory. Most of the world turns its back upon the land of the Green Dragon. It is a dead land, they say.

In the land of fire, smoke, and ash, green begins to sprout upon the wasteland, in the hidden places, beneath the rocks. A new people, a strange people emerge. They are invisible people, forest people, hill people, people who look out from mushrooms, people of legend who were surely there before the people called Americans. Changed, they have become almost unrecognizable to themselves, people who walk with ghosts and walk with Faerie folk. The world turns its eyes away from them, pulls closer together, and feels chilled by their presence behind their backs.

Pockets remain where the evil ones consider themselves rulers of the land of the Green Dragon, the land of the Eagle. They consider themselves the leaders of this land, these evil ones who cry out to the Ten-Headed Dragon who, in illusionary name only, rules the land once known as America. These new people, the new Americans, pay them no attention. The evil ones have no power; they are merely for show. These politicians stay within their small communities, with soldiers about them, but they and their soldiers are afraid to step out of their cities, and they stay closely packed together. They peer into the wilderness fearfully, afraid of their own shadows.

The Return of Arthur and Gwenhwyfar

I stand now in the land of the Green Dragon, and I wear a green cloak and hood. A ball of energy hovers over my head, almost like fire, and over the tip of my staff is a ball of flame. I am in the woods, and it is wintertime. The limbs are bare or perhaps burnt. My breath is icy, and the air is cold. I see a white horse. When he snorts, the cold air turns his breath to mist. I watch, and now I begin to see downtown Asheville, the area called Pack Square. People are fighting and sliding on the ice. There does not seem to be a great deal of snow, just ice.

I see a young man with long, thick hair and a full beard. Braids are woven into his hair. He wears white and sits upon the back of a white horse, hacking at people with a home-forged war hammer. It has a long handle and he is striking people with it, knocking them down. It is almost like watching the movie, *Gangs of New York*, because people are everywhere fighting with whatever they can lay hands on. These gangs of the future seem, in fact, to have been inspired by that movie from the year 2002. The young man on horseback holds a shield upon his arm. Others ride behind him, big men on horseback, knocking people down. They are fighting their way through the crowd with their own weapons, and occasional shots are fired. The young man himself draws a pistol from his belt and fires. Some in the crowd are law enforcement officers or soldiers, so I do not understand why a big gun battle is not in progress. Some of the men fire from horse-back, but it appears people do not have ready access to bullets.

I am there, but not on horseback. I have been knocked off my horse, so I am fighting with my staff. Two of the men on horses notice I am standing on the ground. They come and try to form a wall on one side of me. I finally throw down my staff and begin to use the club I carry. I swing it with both hands, in a frenzy, not at the men on the horses, but at the people on the ground. Someone brings a spirited horse in my direction, but I have trouble mounting it. The young man with the beard is now on the ground, trying to help me mount. Someone next to him grabs me by the collar and pulls me onto the horse. Then they surround the young man and pull him up into his saddle. They are trying to survive, but they also have a sense of humor about the situation. I realize then that the young man on horseback is Arthur, the once and future king.

A shout comes from one of the side streets, and a group of people on foot comes charging in. They are running in formation, and they begin to crash into the side of the mob that is trying to kill us. Arthur swings his horse about. The only horses nearby are those we ride, but now I see other horses coming from a different street, and they begin to fall into a pattern. I hear another shout, and a third group of men on foot arrives. They also appear to be under Arthur's guidance. The three groups of people form into a wedge shape, one group with horses and two groups on foot, and the crowd is hit from all sides.

Some in the crowd are throwing bricks, and others are trying to aim with shotguns. Some are shot, while others go down with arrows in their chests. Some go down beneath the horses. The mob begins to scatter. I see some women in this crowd, but I sense these people are hard and would kill for any reason at all. They are scattering, running, but they are pursued by the men on horses, and most do not escape. Those few who have survived the battle now lie bloody upon the ground. Arthur has blood on his clothing and a grim, unhappy look on his face. We share a feeling of sadness, and I do not know what we will do with all of these people, many of whom now lie dead in the streets.

I see a blood-soaked Rebel flag lying on the ground beneath a large man's body. I sense this small group was one of several that tried, for a time, to control the downtown area of Asheville. These various groups are not much more than gangs. They see themselves as something much greater, but all they did was rape and pillage the people. Arthur is the only one who has gone beyond the concept of gang and has acquired something of an army. Arthur wears white, sometimes with a red dragon. He is known as the Scots party, the Welsh party, the Irish party, the mad Celts. People are attracted to Arthur and Gwenhwyfar by the Arthurian legend. It pulls people to them, but Arthur is much more than a symbol.

The vision changes—we are in downtown Asheville again, but it is later, after even more destruction has occurred. Lili and I are walking together with Arthur and Gwenhwyfar. We are handing out food and bandages to people in Pack Square. Young men and women are waiting to sign up for Arthur's army. Interstate 40, the road up the mountains to Asheville, is blocked off by a wall put there by Arthur's people. They are stationed in stone towers all along that road, and people must go past these towers, past the soldiers in the towers, and then through a wide gate if they wish to enter the protected area. Soldiers are also stationed in Black

Mountain, a small town just inside the wall. They are Arthur's people, and they are welcome there.

More music and entertainers fill the streets, because people who once worked indoors at their computers are now working outdoors, trying to make a living. Younger people are pulling older people through the streets using Japanese-style bicycles. I glimpse a large wagon being pulled down one of the main streets by oxen, but mostly I see bicycles and people walking. Some small vehicles that look almost like cars can be found in the streets, but they stall frequently, and people must often good-naturedly push them out of the way. Just a few of these mini-cars can be seen, and soon there are none. Alternative technology does not seem to work too well in the beginning.

I see a parade of Arthur and Gwenhwyfar's soldiers, men and women, some on horseback and some marching down the street. Arthur and Gwenhwyfar ride in front, and we ride behind them. My riding skills seem to have improved, since this time I remain firmly seated upon my horse. The horses are decorated handsomely, and people are cheering. Later, I see a Maypole standing right in the center of one of the main streets. People are dancing around this pole, and I see smiles and laughter. Although people are wearing layered clothing, I think it is spring.

Trains begin to come into the mountains. They are powered by wood or coal, and people soon begin to use them for travel. I also see a vehicle that resembles a stagecoach, and it can travel long distances. Most people, however, still walk or ride bicycles. Many of the bicycles have three and four wheels, almost like little Model-T cars with canvas-like covers, but they run with bicycle power and not with engines.

I see Arthur and Gwenhwyfar walking up the steps of a local mansion that, before the changes, was an impressive tourist attraction. Cheering crowds of people form rows on either side of them and throw confetti. We walk behind them, with smart-looking soldiers, both male and female, walking on either side. Much of the furniture in the mansion has been cleared out to make room for people to walk back and forth through the hallways. One of the hallways has been emptied of tables, and it is filled with people. Arthur and Gwenhwyfar take turns speaking to them, but the crowds are so large, they cannot all fit inside.

In the open fields, I see soldiers on horseback and on foot, marching and twirling, practicing. I hear one of the older soldiers complaining to a younger soldier. He tells him that, for the first year, bullets and gunpowder worked really well. What he really means is that bullets worked well for the first six or eight months, and, back then, you needed them to protect yourself. At some point after that, for some odd reason that makes no sense to anyone, gunpowder just stopped working the way it had before. One bullet would work, but the next one would not fire, and so guns became untrustworthy. The energy has begun to change, and certain things are just not allowed to work now. Humans cannot kill from afar as easily anymore.

The vision changes once more, and Lili and I are standing together with Arthur and Gwenhwyfar. An emissary has been sent by the Evil One, an officer from one of his troops. This man has come to inform us it would be best to allow a friendly agreement, a friendly occupation. He says we should allow some of the Evil One's troops in to help keep the peace. This emissary of the Evil One tells us he wishes to offer protection and to provide for our technological needs. He offers money and food and gifts if Arthur and Gwenhwyfar will allow troops in and accept willingly and verbally the Evil One's sovereignty over the area. He tells us we would be allowed to run the area independently, with only a small number of the Evil One's troops present to act as governors or peacekeepers.

As a matter of fact, peace at that time is quite well kept already, and it is safe to walk the streets at night. The Evil One's troops are not needed in Asheville or in nearby areas. Transportation has improved, and people have learned to adapt to their changed lifestyles. Arthur's protected area extends quite a long distance from Asheville, even into the bordering states of Tennessee, Virginia, and Georgia. The territorial borders are decided primarily by which geological formations provide the best walls.

The emissary's offer is rejected, and he is sent away. Though Arthur's men want to throw him out bodily by the seat of his pants, he is allowed to leave with dignity. He offers Arthur a gift, but Arthur does not accept it, nor will he even touch it. He tells the man, "We do not need the Devil's help in protecting and governing the land of Appalachia." The emissary, highly indignant and angry, stalks out. Arthur has told him, and it is already well known, that the Evil One cannot send in troops without our agreement. We are protected by Arthur and Gwenhwyfar's troops, but our true protection comes from the Mother and Father and Jesus. They are the true shield walls of Appalachia, and Arthur rules in their name and by their leave.

The Golden Years

Angus and Kat are two very ancient Gnome Travelers, who also happen to be Gwladys' parents. They are known as Travelers because they have already taken the pathway to the realm of the Mother and Father Creator and Jesus, and so they can now travel back and forth at will. They have returned to Tír na nÓg for a time to help with preparations for the approaching changes. Though they are much older than it is possible for Humans to imagine, they appear as though they are still in their early twenties. Since Angus and Kat have already spent much time with the Holy Family, we thought it appropriate they should speak of the golden years that will arrive upon Christ's return to the physical Mother Earth.

"After Jesus' return, Humanity will notice several astounding changes in their environment. One of the most notable changes will be in the air itself. The very air will give off the presence of peace. No longer will there be the chaotic energy of your machines constantly barraging your environment outdoors and indoors with their communications. Their ceaseless energy, which flows through your entire world and even through your own person, will come to an abrupt halt. This alone will bring great relief from the stress caused by these energies. Humanity has been ceaselessly barraged by this unnatural energy for so long that you have become unaware of its presence, but it is taking its toll. This dark, unnatural, almost frenzied energy has been causing great hidden torment to your physical body, to your mind, and to your spirit.

"This energy has even caused the animals to settle into an uneasy acceptance of it within their environment. This machine energy, which is barely perceptible to the Human senses, has caused the vegetation upon Mother Earth to become less vibrant and healthy than it was in the past. It is most hoped that, after reading these words, you will begin to attune your senses to this energy and realize that it has no place in the Creation of the Mother and Father. Therefore, this manmade energy will cease upon Jesus' return.

"Humanity will at first notice a deafening silence and a great relief of burdens upon their spirit. The sudden death of the machine energy will bring freedom to the spirit and to the body and uplift the heart of Humanity and of all Creation. Natural machines that work for Humanity are different from unnatural machines that enslave Humanity, but I will not go into detail about that at this time. With the absence of unnatural machines,

Humanity will finally be able to hear, understand, and comprehend the language of the animals, the language of the trees and other green things, the language of Mother Earth, and, most importantly, the language of the Mother and Father Creator and Jesus. For the first time in many untold ages, Humanity will be able to hear directly the words of the Mother and Father and Jesus spoken to them. They will comprehend these words with great spiritual clarity.

"Humanity will also be able to hear the beautiful songs of Creation, which can, at this very moment, be heard throughout all the realms. Humanity will be able to hear the songs of Angels as they sing praises of joy to the Mother, Father, and Jesus. Instead of the distant hum or grumble or shriek of your machines, Humanity will, if they wish, in the quiet moments, be able to attune to this beautiful, holy music which can be heard in Heaven and on Earth and throughout all Creation.

"I have earlier stated to you that the presence of peace will be felt within the very air itself. Again, for the first time in untold ages, instead of negative emotions such as anger, fear, lust, and other such emotions running rampant, Humans will be able to think clearly and control the raging fires within them. This will not be the drug-induced peace that many of your physicians supply to their patients. A natural peace will emanate from Jesus and from the Mother and Father, and Humans will be able to accept and dwell within this peace. The desire to make war will no longer be a part of the Human psyche.

"Because Humans will be connected to the Mother and Father and Jesus, they will be able to see more clearly with their spirit eyes. Therefore, the colors of Creation will become more apparently vibrant. Though Human eyes can see many colors now, compared to those people who can see clearly with their spirit eyes, it is as if Humanity sees the world in shades of black and white. Within Creation is a combination of colors you cannot even comprehend. These beautiful colors will make their presence known to you within the lushness of the land. Through the colors of the trees, the bright beauty of flowers, the blueness of the sky, and the golden rays of the sun, endless new colors will be found throughout all Creation. The beauty Humanity will find around them will sear their hearts with an overwhelming sense of awe and thankfulness for the artistic and incomprehensible beauty in the hands of the Mother and Father Creator. Of course, this lush, vibrant beauty, this wellness, this wholeness of Creation will come from the presence of Jesus upon the Earth.

"Humanity will turn from being an industrial people to become, once again, an agrarian society throughout the entire world. Were Humanity to become an agrarian society now, it would cause much hardship, for you have become weak in body and spirit, and the food you consume does not truly nourish you and give you the life-sustaining energy you need. Because of the healing changes throughout Creation, Humanity will become reenergized. They will be able to perform tasks with great ease that before would be considered by them to be impossible to do without the use of machines. Upon eating the fruits of their labor, the food they have planted and harvested themselves, they will become even more energized, for the food will truly provide nourishment to the body and the spirit in its purest essence.

"Cities will fade away or be transformed into smaller communities. Lush vegetation will bury many cities beneath green vines and flowers, and Humans will come together in smaller groups, villages, and smaller towns. Surprisingly, the Earth will appear much vaster than it is now. Humans will find there is room enough for everyone and that the need for crowding no longer exists. Humans will live longer than they do now—much, much longer—and, in that way, they will become more like us, the Fair Folk. Children will still be born, and there will be room for them. There will be no poverty upon the Earth. There will be neither sickness, nor death, as you know it.

"Upon the Holy Days, Humans will, through natural means, hear the calling of the Mother and Father and Jesus, and they will make pilgrimages to the court of Jesus in the Holy City of Jerusalem. These will be great festive holidays with much singing and dancing and gratitude and joyfulness. Though Jesus' capital will be in the Holy City of Jerusalem, he will neglect no one with his loving presence and will travel throughout all of Creation. He will be found discussing the techniques of farming with the farmer in the field, attending community gatherings in small towns and villages, breaking bread in the homes of simple folk, and playing with the children in the meadows. You see, Jesus will be the loving king and brother of all folk, be they rulers of kingdoms or peaceful farmers of the land. He will be found spending most of his time with down-to-earth people.

"All of Creation will rest within the very heart of the peacefulness of the Mother and Father and Jesus for one thousand years, until the time when the Evil One once again rises from the depths of Hell and makes one last, pathetic effort to reclaim Creation. There will be a tremendous battle, but he and his followers will be completely and utterly destroyed. Mother Earth and all of Creation will be transformed and reborn, to enter an endless age of loving peace that will endure for all eternity.

"The first coming thousand years of peace on Earth are not that far away. None of us knows the exact date, not even Jesus himself, but the Mother and Father know. It will happen when it happens, but be aware and be awake and be alert. Times of trouble and times of tribulation are coming, but they will be a brief few years compared to the glorious years that follow. Mother and Father's Blessings from Kat and Angus, the Traveling Gnomes."

CHAPTER XV

The Twelve Strands

The twelve strand teachings, as described by Gwladys and Henry, form a vital part of the Faerie spiritual teachings. In the days of coming changes, you may find these teachings a source of comfort and help.

The Three Strands of Autumn
    1. Gathering in the harvest
    2. Preparation, making your burrow snug
    3. Clarity, knowing where you are, thanksgiving
The Three Strands of Winter
    4. Resting
    5. Remembering old stories, reflecting on life
    6. Joy, recognition of coming son/sun
The Three Strands of Spring
    7. Planting the seed
    8. Birth, awakening, resurrection
    9. Enjoyment of life to the fullest
The Three Strands of Summer
    10. Strength
    11. Work, tending one's own garden
    12. Taking care of others' gardens

"The twelve strands are also known as the twelve strands of life. We have many other strands, but these will help you move through your Human life. Consider these strands as a ship's compass, a map, a prominent landmark, a peak in the distance where you can look to orient yourself, a star far above in the heavens, or the movement of the sun, moon, and stars above you. Once you learn them, not only in your mind, but in your heart, they will be a dependable, proper guide and will lead you through troubled times. The twelve strands, much like the ten commandments, are a gift from the Holy Parents and Christ and Mary. The twelve strands, unlike the ten commandments, are not cords to bind and tie you. Rather, you might say they represent harp strings, which, when plucked, create the sound of harmony, so that you, and all those who move by the strands and make use of them, live in Creation with the sound of harmony.

"All that exists is substance, and substance is all energy. The way we of the Fair Folk understand it is that energy is a substance that exists in waves, waves of love from the Holy Parents. In the beginning, the Holy Parents came together and formed a seed that was dropped in a still pond of nothingness or the void, and the ripples from the seed, which later became Jesus, rippled out and Creation was born. We see all existence as waves of love. Therefore, when one strand is plucked, or a group of strands is plucked, it forms a movement of waves of energy, of magic, of love, and creates a working of harmony in Creation. If the strands are ignored or brushed roughly aside, or if you force your way between them as most Humans do, you are not working in harmony with Creation. You are not playing a beautiful song that is pleasing to the Holy Parents or Jesus or Mary. You are violating and enslaving, or attempting to enslave, Creation herself. Therefore, learn to play the harp of harmony, which has twelve strands. Begin as a novice; gently and with reverence, pluck the strands, and learn the sound of their notes, and joy will fill your Grail or heart cup. The blessings, the living water, will overflow your cup with love and spill out to all Creation.

"Therefore, to understand the strands, it is a good concept to see them strung upon a beautifully-carved harp. We will not tell you what color the harp is or what is carved upon it. That is for you to decide. It is for you to design your harp in your mind and your heart and your spirit. It may be a golden harp or a harp of beautifully carved wood, but what is important is that it is your harp, created by you as a reflection of your spirit. Upon your harp, string the twelve strands of harmony. This teaching is not a mere gimmick, an empty shallow thing, for, once you create this harp in your mind, in your heart, and in your spirit, and you string the harp with the twelve strands of harmony, you actually create the harp of harmony in your soul. It is a gift given to you by the Holy Parents and Christ and Mary to comfort you, to keep your spirits high, and to act as a compass in troubled times. Of course, it is not the only tool or gift given to you by the Holy Parents, but it is a rather nice one, I must say.

"All of Creation enjoys music. To put it in Human terms, all Humans are guided or moved by music, whether they enjoy music or not. For those who enjoy music, music is their guide for the very fact that it moves them. If the music is pure or uplifting, it can guide them through troubled times, heal them or comfort them, or make them laugh and dance and sing. Music is always a guide, no matter if it is positive music that uplifts beings and draws them closer to the Holy Parents and Christ and Mary, or if it is music filled with darkness, with no light within, which can instead lead one down the wrong pathways to the Evil One in whom dwells no mother. Either way, music is a guide. Music is a wave that can uplift one's spirit and inspire one to do the works of the Holy Parents, Christ, and Mary. On the other hand, this wave can also carry one to the Evil One if one performs works of evil and becomes crushed upon the rocks of inhumanity. Therefore, learn to play the harp of harmony, that you may not be led astray.

"The harp of harmony, as is proper, is a circle, and the circle represents all Creation. The twelve strings are divided into four sets or groupings of three. Each set or grouping represents a season of the Great Mother Earth, and three strands within each grouping or set represent the great concepts of that season. Because the harp of harmony reflects Creation, as is the will of the Holy Parents and Christ and Mary, there is no first string. It is cyclical, and the first string always begins where you are now. Today, we will begin with the first string of autumn, though even this does not always follow a set pattern, for sometimes we may need to pluck a string or a group of strings that is found in another time of the year. If the need is there, please play the strings. This teaching is not to be carved in stone or bound in chains.

The Three Strands of Autumn

"The three strands of autumn are clarity, gathering in the harvest, and preparation. Clarity is concerned with the crispness of the autumn air. It is the time of year when the smoldering heat of summer suddenly gives way to the cool, clean, crispness of the autumn wind. This wind brings your senses to life or wakes them up as the cold air is felt upon your skin. It is also a time when you begin to take more care of yourself by bundling yourself in warmer clothing. That crispness or clearness of the air also represents clear thinking in your mind. The confusion of the past year is driven away. It is as if the cold autumn wind has passed through your spirit and cleaned all the confusion from you, and you can experience clear thinking. You can look back, if you pluck the strings in the proper manner, on your life—what you have accomplished, your successes, and what you perceive to be your failures—with an open heart, not with judgmental flogging of yourself, but with compassion and love shown to you by the Holy Parents.

"Also, with the strand of clear autumn thinking, you can look to the future, and learn to dream again, as you dreamt once when you were a child. With this strand, you can look to the future and prepare, no matter what age you are, no matter if you are a young child or an ancient elder. The strand of clear thinking will also help you perceive thankfulness for the blessings the Holy Parents and Christ and Mary have poured into your Grail, into your very heart's cup itself, so the blessings may overflow and spill out to all Creation that you may share your bounty in thanksgiving. In so doing, you will, as the Christians say, count your blessings, and give thanks for them to the Holy Parents, Christ, and Mary. Many times when your life does not seem too blessed, if you will start to count your blessings one by one, you will come to see that your cup, in fact, is overflowing. No matter where you are or who you are in life, you can always share your bounty or thankfulness with someone who has less than you, for, sadly, someone will always have less than you.

"The second strand, which is interwoven with this first strand, is harvesting. You begin to harvest all that you planted in the year and in years gone by. This is when you begin to gather in your harvest, not only your physical harvest, but your spirit harvest. This could apply to you as an individual if you have harvested good seed in years gone by, for you will harvest rich, nourishing food to help feed your physical and spiritual self. If you have harvested bad seed, you will have to struggle a little harder to be sure you plant good seed in the coming year. Still, it is not a time to flog yourself, but, instead, a time to realize that, with the Holy Parents, Christ, and Mary guiding you with the twelve strands, you can still plant better seeds next year. Every harvest brings a blessing of some sort, and you begin to gather in these blessings. You begin to prepare a table of thankfulness that you may share with others, not only with loved ones, family, and friends, but also with those who have less than you. What you have left, you will store away for yourself and your family that you may survive through the long winter until the time you can plant new seed in spring.

"The third autumn strand of harmony is preparation, preparing for the long winter. This harp string, when it is plucked, helps you to prepare your home for the long winter to ensure that your burrow, or your home, is secure, snug, and warm. Therefore, not only do you check your physical home and tend to its needs that it may ride out the long winter without your venturing out into the snow to attempt to fix something that could have been fixed during autumn, but you also tend to your physical body. During this time, you should exercise more, ensure that you are eating the proper foods, and, still, though the weather is turning cold, get out in nature and enjoy the fresh face of the Mother Earth as much as possible. Commune with nature. It is also time to tend to your burrow of spirit or that spiritual home within you, and by doing so you strengthen the communication between you and the Holy Parents and Christ and Mary. You ensure that the pathways of your heart to them have been swept clear of all debris that you may travel to them, and they to you, easily.

"During this time of year, we feast, and we bring in the harvest of our labors as far as food supplies. We do have feasts of thanksgiving, we do share our bounty with others, and we put aside the extra bounty we have left over, so that we may go through the winter, though the winters in Tír na nÓg are not hard like the winters in your physical world. We tend to prepare our physical homes or burrows for the winter and to ensure they are warm, snug and cozy. We also prepare ourselves physically to be sure our physical bodies are in the best possible condition they can be in, that we may travel through the winter in comfort with as few aches and pains as possible. We also prepare our spiritual burrows and perform any tending that needs to be done to them, with the help of the Holy Parents, Christ and Mary, that our spirits may be warm, snug, and cozy in the light and warmth of their love.

"As you can see, the three strands of clarity, gathering in the harvest, and preparation form a fine strong cord of autumn.

The Three Strands of Winter

"The three strands of winter are the strands of rest, remembering old stories and reflection on past events and joy, and the recognizing of the coming of the son of the Holy Parents. The strand of rest means that you have worked hard all year long, and, now that the weather has forced you indoors, you have more time for rest and recuperation. You stay comfortable and snug in your home before the roaring fireplace. The time of rest is letting go of all worries, fears, and guilt, letting go and giving these concerns into the hands of the Holy Parents. Not only do you physically rest in winter, but you also rest spiritually. Perhaps a good picture of this would be someone sitting in their rocking chair or a nice comfortable chair, their head tilted forward with their chin on their chest, sound asleep and with a look of peace on their face. The winter strand is like a still lake covered with ice, where there is no movement, and everything is still and quiet and peaceful.

"The winter strand represents a well-deserved rest and the regrouping of energy, so that with the coming spring you will be able to carry on with your business and with your tasks. In the case of one who is looking into the garden gates of the spirit world, it is a time to be cheerful, for you will soon be traveling the spirit pathway back home to the garden. It is not a time to be afraid, but a time to look forward to with great joy. Therefore, the winter strand of rest is not so much the end of a strand; instead, the strand forms a circle or a hoop. The winter strand of rest is always the preparation for the continuance of life, whether it be Human life in the physical world in preparation for spring or spirit life in the spirit world. The winter strand of rest is not the end, but merely the next step to the beginning. During the time of winter when you are indoors protecting yourself from the cold, you have your loved ones or your friends gathered about you. Even if you live by yourself, in actuality you are never alone, for caring companions are with you at all times. Whether it be the Holy Parents, Christ, Mary, Angels, we of the Fair Folk, or family members who walk the spirit pathway, compassionate company is with you always.

"With the strand of reflection, or remembering old stories and tales, you sit with your friends and family, and you speak of times gone by, whether it be your life or the lives of others. You tell the stories of your family and your culture, the stories of friends or of your own life, the joyful stories, and, if need be, the sad stories. Still, let there be more joyful stories than sad stories, so your winter months indoors will be filled with joy instead of sadness. It is not a time for looking back, but it is a time for remembering and sharing the stories with those who come after you, so that the stories may not be forgotten. Yes, you could write them down; you could put them in one of your machines, but it would never be the same as when the story is told straight from the mouth of the storyteller to the ears of the listener. A bard's stories do not shine as brilliantly, touch us as deeply, or carry us as far as they do when they are told directly by the bard's mouth. The sound of the voice and the words opens the gate and condenses or collapses time, so that it has no meaning. You journey there with the storyteller, and you become a traveler. Though we love our books, there is nothing like a good story told straight from the lips of a storyteller.

"Reflection is also remembering. If you are at the end of your life, you are in the winter of your life. One's winter does not need to begin when the body is bent with age, for the winter of one's life can come early in the lifetime. Should you find yourself in the winter of your life, and you know you will not see spring, this becomes a time for reflection—reflection, but not judgment, for if the Holy Parents or Christ or Mary do not condemn you, why should you condemn yourself? It is a time to look on the past of your life, whether it be a long life or short life, and ponder where you have fallen short of your desire, but focus more on where you have succeeded. Let the pain of the past which causes you grief or wounds go. Let the pain be carried away by the holy stream of life; let it float or be carried out away from your sight. Let it go, for it is not important anymore, nor was it truly important when it first happened to you, that situation which caused you pain.

"It is interesting, when Humans are about to cross through the pathway gates into the spirit world, how the most painful of memories, which have plagued them their entire lives, do not seem to matter anymore, as though they do not hold any importance at all. I am not saying you should not grieve for your pain and ponder the wounds you were given during your life. I am saying do not dwell on them, and at the time when you cross through the gates into the Garden, these past wounds will not mean anything to you. If Humans could only learn this before they pass through the gates into the Garden, it would make their life here on physical Earth more blessed, not only for them, but also for all Creation. So if you are in the winter of your lifetime, reflect on your life with compassion, love, and respect. Take the good you have earned from this life, even though it be a small treasure, and if it appears to you that you do not have much good to collect from your life, even a small treasure is a treasure. See those moments of happiness in your life as treasures and remember the words that 'even a small treasure is a treasure.'

"Though the winter strand of remembering or reflection is looking back, it is also a pathway through the gates of looking forward. Therefore, as you reflect over your life or even over the past year, you look forward to the springtime or passing through the gates of a new beginning. The Holy Parents have decreed that the course of life itself may run in a circle. Therefore, with the strand of remembering and reflection also comes the strand of looking forward to the future with gladness of heart and expectation. The winter strand of remembrance and reflection, as with all other strands, is not an end, but the beginning of a pathway into a new adventure or journey. Therefore, the strands always form a circle and run continu-ously, never stopping, as you see in a Celtic knot. The three strands we wear about our waist as priest and priestess, the rope belt, is tied three times, but the belt itself forms a circle about our waist.

"The last strand of winter is the strand of joy. Now, as you remember, the strands are formed into a circle. More than two thousand years ago, all of Creation awaited the birth of the Messiah, who was found in Jesus, otherwise known as the Christ. Creation is again looking forward to his return, that he may bring with him the spirit Garden, so that it may merge or become one with the physical Garden, the physical Earth. Therefore, this strand of joy represents that merging. This is why, in this time of year, you begin to look forward to or anticipate the arrival of Christ Mass. Before the birth of Christ, many thousands of years ago, the people (and I am referring to all Creation) looked forward to the return of the physical sun that lights the sky during the day, and Jesus is a reflection of this tradition. You might say that the very sun himself was prophesying the coming of the son of the Holy Parents. During this time of year, the nights were short, and there was more physical darkness on the Earth than light, more nighttime than day-time. It was close to this time of year, during the Winter Solstice, that the people of old celebrated the return of the physical sun. This later became a celebration of Christ Mass or the birth of Christ.

"Joy is also a strand to be shared with others, and this is reflected in your time today in the giving of gifts and the decoration of trees or homes with bright, shiny objects reflecting the return of the sun. This is the time of the year to gather those you love close about you, or to be gathered close about to the ones you love, and, even for those with no physical family, to remember you are never alone, but have family and loving companions always near you. It is a time not only to be thankful for the blessings given to you by the Holy Parents, Christ, and Mary and all Creation, but also to be thankful for the very gift of existence or life itself. During this time of year, you share joy with your loved ones, whether they are the Holy Parents themselves, Christ or Mary, those loved ones of spirit, the physical loved ones who grow with you on the Earth, or the Great Mother Earth and all her children. Joy dwells within your heart, and your home and your heart begin to shine brilliantly like an ornament on a tree, becoming brighter and brighter and brighter, as bright as the sun on a cold, dark, wintry day, so that others may see your light, and, if they are in need, they may come to you. You share with them what you can, and your light reminds others to increase their own joy and light, so that the sun may return once again. Therefore, as the old saying goes, 'Light a candle, so you do not curse the darkness.'

"As you can see, the three strands of rest, reflection, and the recognizing of the coming of the Son form a fine strong cord of winter.

The Three Strands of Spring

"The three strands of spring are birth, the planting of the seed, and enjoyment of life to the fullest. Springtime is widely known as a time when the buds begin to appear on all blooming things. The snows have gone, the weather has become warm, and everything begins to bloom. It is the time of year of many births. It is a time of hope. It is a time of passing from the darkness to the light, from death into rebirth. Again, even those beings entering or leaving the winter of their lives and moving into physical death can look forward to springtime or the rebirth of themselves in spirit or even in another physical body. Either way, the death of winter is not the end, but the beginning of the birth of spring. It is a time of resurrection, the time of the resurrection of Jesus who rose from the tomb after his crucifixion, a time of hope and bright light and extreme joy.

"It is a beginning. It is like a fresh-faced young child staring at all Creation with wonder in his or her eyes. This is what springtime and rebirth is, the time of a clean slate, a new beginning, a time of innocence when one can look forward to hopeful potential in the far distance. During this time of rebirth, the child feels no limits and sees only magic about her. She does not need to wear, at least not yet, the chains of commitments or illusory bindings that enslave her parents in the Human world, weighing down their lives with misery. The child stands there in the bright sunlight, a young bud ready to begin life once more, a newborn being who only feels joy and wonder at the magical creation about her. It is also a time of resurrection, a time of new beginnings, not only for newborn creatures, but for the very old as well, for even an old person at the end of their life can have a new beginning, a springtime in the midst of a winter storm.

"Springtime, also, is a time for the planting of the seed, those hoped-for potentials which are small seeds you plant in your life in the soil of the Great Mother. In the spirit world, the seed you plant is in the heart of the Holy Parents and Christ and Mary, and it is the seed they plant in you. To reach that potential, whether it be a physical crop, a new heart or Grail, a new outlook on life, a new beginning, or to be born again, you must plant the seed. That hopeful potential, that small seed, perhaps tinier than a grain of sand, still can grow into a great tree or beautiful flowering plant if you have the faith. Springtime, therefore, is also the small seed of faith or potential.

"Springtime is also a time to enjoy life to its fullest. You have survived the cold winter of your life, whether it be a physical winter or a spiritual winter. Beauty is all around you, and all life blooms and begins anew. It is a time of high magic filled with sunny, bright days, warm winds, and beautiful bird songs in the trees. The time of spring makes even the very old feel young again. They may even want to dance or at least consider it. It is the time of year when the Great Mother is very fertile and very vigorous. This fertility is also shown in having the energy from the long winter's rest to begin to plant the seed, to begin the work, so that you may one day have a large crop or a great harvest. Not only is there energy to do your work to prepare the seed for the coming year or to plant the seed, but you also have energy to dance and to sing and for feasting, for your heart in springtime dances in glee, whether you want it to or not.

"This time of year, springtime, is a time for music and happy songs. It is a time to welcome back the sun that shines brightly on your face, as it is also a time to remember the coming or the return of the son of the Holy Parents, Christ Jesus. It is a time filled with promise. Springtime is a good time to begin a work of harmony. Now, remember, the realm of springtime can be experienced during any time of the year. It does not matter if it is the dead of winter, for you can still bring spring to your household and to your life.

"As you can see, the three strands of birth, the planting of the seed, and enjoyment of life to the fullest form a fine strong cord of springtime.

The Three Strands of Summer

"The three strands of summer are strength, work and tending your own garden, and taking care of others' gardens. The first strand of strength speaks of a time in summer when the crops are strong or growing, when you are at the peak of your strength, young and powerful, and you feel confident in your abilities. Hard work does not mean difficulty to you, and you are able to carry your load and to carry others' loads as well. The summer strand of strength speaks not only of the strength of the physical body (and the physical body can represent any physical being), but it also represents the strength of the spirit, or that you are at peace with the Holy Parents and, therefore, at peace within yourself. Not only do you have the strength to carry out the tasks appointed to you, but you also have the strength to share with others.

"The second strand is the companion of strength, for with strength you are able to work and tend your garden. In other words, you can see to the physical needs of yourself and your family or those loved ones around you. You can ensure they have food to eat and shelter over their heads, are safe and snug in the arms of your life, and have a place in your heart Grail, but you also will meet their spiritual needs to the best of your ability. This is called tending the garden. It also means tending a physical garden, for everyone should have his or her own physical garden. By tending a garden, you can learn to become closer to the Great Mother Earth, learn to speak to the soil, and hear the whisper of your Mother as you place your hands into the soil. Tending a physical garden is a way of learning to work in harmony with all nature, and, by working in harmony with all nature, you learn to work or to be in harmony with your own self.

"Not only do you meet the needs of yourself and your family through the strength of tending your own garden, but you also have extra energy to help tend the gardens of those about you. This means you may go next door to your neighbors, to those in need, and help them with their physical garden, and, if needed, their spiritual garden to help meet their needs. You can do this for you have extra strength in summertime. In the summertime of your life, the Holy Parents always give you extra energy, so that not only may you have the energy to tend the needs of the ones most important to you, but to also tend to the needs of others about you, whether these needs be physical or spiritual. You will not only be able to tend to the needs of your family and others about you, but also tend to the needs of the Great Mother Earth and to all Creation. You will have the strength to stand up to those who wish to enslave your Mother Earth, kill all her children or enslave them, kill and steal all green things from them and from your sight, and fill your air with poison, that you or your children or other children of the Great Mother and the Holy Parents will not be able to draw breath and so will die. You will be able to stand strong against these lords of death and, with a strong heart and a brave heart, tend to the garden of all Creation.

"Therefore, the three strands of summer form a very strong cord tied about the waist of a warrior, for the time of summer is the time of the warrior. Remember, there are both female warriors and male warriors in our realm, as there should be, and as there are in your Human realm as well. Again, the three strands of summer or the cord of summer is not limited to the proper season itself, but may be called upon and requested as your ally and worn in battle as a strong cord about your waist during any time of the year.

The Twelve Strand Cord

"We have given you the twelve strands. These twelve strands form a strong cord that is worn about the waist of the Holy Parents and of Christ and Mary and all Creation. It is a circle—never ending, always living, immortal. It is a circle never tainted by death, but holding rebirth and immortality. These twelve strands form the root of the Great Tree. Starting from a small seed deep in the womb of the Great Mother Earth, they form into four great roots of three, and these four great roots of three form the sapling, the trunk, the great branches that reach out over all Creation and provide shelter for all Creation beneath the Great Tree's boughs. Within its leaf-covered limbs, you will find the homes of all the birds of Creation, and they sing a sweet song, the story of Creation from its beginning until its end, though its end will never come. In the womb of his mother, Mary, was placed the seed of Jesus, and the seed grew into a strong tree and then into the Great Tree and then into the tree of life and then into the tree of rebirth and resurrection. The Great Tree is a reflection of the Messiah, who is Jesus Christ, for beneath the boughs of its great arms, we find shelter. In the call of the sweet birdsong voice, we find comfort, and, within his robes of peace, we find rest.

"At the feet of the Holy Parents, there is no religion. The Fair Folk, like Humans, glow with the colors of a prism through which the love of the Holy Parents shines and reflects all the nationalities found upon the physical Earth. We, the Fair Folk, wish to make clear to Humanity that we are a tolerant people. All faiths, no matter if they be Christian, Jewish, Buddhist, Pagan, Islamic, Hindu or any of the other myriad religions found on the face of the physical Earth, are valid in the eyes of the Holy Parents, so long as the practitioners of these faiths live their lives with sincere compassion and love towards all Creation. In the end, when all the dross is swept away by the loving hand of the Holy Parents, what truth will be left is the love that is found in one's heart for God and for all Creation. That is the ultimate truth, the high truth that goes beyond any religious doctrine.

Ceremony of Celebration

"The ceremony which follows can be performed to celebrate any of the Celtic Holy Days, or it may be a simple celebration of the Gathering of the Grove. It is meant to be performed outdoors. The more ornate a ceremony becomes, the more it seems to separate Humans from all Creation. A ceremony of simplicity will bring intimacy with all Creation.

"It is helpful if both a priest and priestess are in attendance, but one person can do this ceremony alone if desired. Suggested items for the ceremony include your staff, a cup of water to represent the Grail Cup, a loaf of bread, and a small bowl of cream or milk.

"Find the center of your yard or another spot where you feel spiritually comfortable. Place your Grail Cup, the loaf of bread, and the vessel of cream upon the Earth in this area. Arrange these items as you wish. Use this area as your sacred spiritual center to begin the ceremony.

"With your staff in one hand, raise your free hand to the sky and speak words similar to these: 'As a child of Earth, Sea, and Sky, I humbly ask the Mother and Father Creator, Jesus, and Mother Mary to bear witness to my ceremony.'

"Lower your free hand to the Earth and say, 'I also humbly acknowledge my Mother Earth who surrounds and sustains me, and I welcome any of my animal family who wish to bear witness to my ceremony. I also humbly ask any friendly Faeries who serve the Mother and Father Creator to bear witness to this ceremony.' You may also wish to request any loving spirit companions of which you are aware to observe your ceremony.

"With your staff, step out and mark the four directions of Mother Earth. Be sure to travel clockwise, and, at each compass point, thump your staff three times, and humbly request that the Guardian Angel of that direction attend your ceremony. Return to the sacred center in your yard.

"Lift the Grail Cup above your head and say, 'Mother and Father Creator, you sustain me with the Living Water of your love. Therefore, with gratefulness, I offer Mother Earth a small drink of living water from my cup.' Pour the water upon the ground.

"Set the cup down, pick up the loaf of bread, and hold it skyward, saying, 'Mother and Father Creator, please bless this bread, that I may humbly offer my cousins in nature a small feast.' Cut the loaf in half. Tear one of the halves into pieces, and use it to feed Mother Earth's children. You may put the other half aside to feast upon when the ceremony is completed.

"Pick up the vessel of cream, and hold it skyward, saying, 'Mother and Father Creator, please bless this cream, so that it may nourish my Faerie family.' You may leave the bowl of cream outside overnight if this is acceptable to do in the location where the ceremony is taking place.

"At this time, in words spoken from your heart, discuss the blessings symbolized by the holiday you are celebrating. End the ceremony with a prayer of your own choosing, and thank the Mother and Father and all the others who attended spiritually and physically. Your farewell can be as simple or complex as you wish."

The Celtic Faerie celebrate the following holidays: Imbolc/Candlemas (February), Ostara/Spring Equinox (March), Easter (April), Beltane (May), Litha/Summer Solstice (June), Lughnasadh/Lammas (August), Mabon/Fall Equinox (September), Samhain/Halloween (October), and Christ-mas/Winter Solstice (December). These are the traditional ancient Celtic holidays, with the addition of Christmas and Easter, which are celebrated in honor of the birth and resurrection of Christ. The dates may differ from year to year, so you will need to consult a calendar to determine the exact dates for the current year.

The Twelve Warrior Strands

The strands that follow were provided by the Fair Folk of the Grove to help Humans draw closer to the Holy Family and to Mother Earth.

1.   In whatever faith you take comfort or find most nourishing to your spirit, learn to return to the loving embrace of the Holy Mother and Father and Christ and Mary, or, if you are not of the Christian faith, to the Mother and Father Creator.

2.   Take an active role in defending the Great Mother Earth by joining a group or starting one of your own.

3.   Become defenders of the defenseless, whether they are Human or animal or green thing or sky or water or any part of Creation.

4.   Always seek knowledge, not only physical knowledge that serves your realm, but also spiritual knowledge. Always seek to learn new things.

5.   Learn to play a musical instrument, and learn to develop your skills in an art of any kind that brings you the greatest sense of accomplishment. Partake of, and enjoy, the arts of others.

6.   Learn to connect to Mother Earth as a proper child should, through the art of gardening or taking walks in nature or becoming what Humans refer to as a naturalist. Become an expert on the ways of your Mother Earth.

7.   Learn to train yourself to become a warrior. Strengthen your body and spirit through exercise, that you may handle the rigors of combat in any physical or spiritual situation. Disdain modern weapons. Instead, favor the use of the staff, of the sword, and of the physical martial arts. In developing these skills, you will learn to grow into a powerful warrior for the Holy Parents, Christ, Mary, and all Creation.

8.   Learn to be a healer, whether it is a healer of Humans, of animals, or of Mother Earth herself. Choose a healing field that captures your heart and interest, and strive to be an expert within it.

9.   Learn to give counsel and take counsel. Learn to be a counselor and to give good advice to those who are troubled. Learn to be a good listener and hear clearly the needs of others, but, also, so that you yourself may receive counsel when needed.

10.   Learn to be a leader when leaders are needed and a follower when followers are needed.

11. Learn to be a peacemaker or ambassador of peace in times of conflict.

12. Whatever path you follow, cultivate the light of the Holy Mother and Father Creator within your own spirit, so that you will be a bright light unto others in a time of darkness.

Prayer of the Fair Folk of the Grove

"We pray to the Holy Parents, Christ, and Mary that they may send down a blessing upon all Creation. We pray that all peoples may learn to hear the loving voice of their Mother and Father Creator. No matter what faith they belong to or what doctrine they put their trust in, we pray from the deepest well in our hearts that they will learn to love their Mother and Father with all their soul, with all their heart, and with all their mind. We also humbly ask of the Holy Family that their lost children learn to cherish their Mother Earth who gave birth to them and, like good children with loving compassion, care for their sick Mother. We pray also that Humanity will finally remember their forgotten Faerie family, and that one day, in our Mother and Father's Garden, we will join hands and gaze upon each other's faces with hearts filled with joy at our reunion.

"We pray that, whatever path you take in life, may it be the path of peace. In Christ's name, Amen."

How to Learn More

Please visit our website if you would like to:

✧ Discover more of the Celtic Faerie teachings,

✧ Learn when new books become available, or

✧ Join in celebrations to honor the ancient Celtic holidays at Avalon Grove in the North Carolina mountains.

www.avalongrove.com

Made in the USA
Columbia, SC
12 March 2023

13663125R00143